# Engineering applications
of computational hydraulics—volume II
*Homage to Alexandre Preissmann*

# Numerical models
in environmental fluid mechanics

## Other books in this series

# Engineering applications of computational hydraulics vol II
## *Homage to Alexandre Preissmann*

*Edited by* **MB Abbott and JA Cunge**

**Numerical models in environmental fluid mechanics**

# J-P Benqué, A Hauguel, P-L Viollet

Electricité de France, Chatou

**Pitman Advanced Publishing Program**
BOSTON · LONDON · MELBOURNE

PITMAN BOOKS LIMITED
128 Long Acre, London WC2E 9AN

PITMAN PUBLISHING INC
1020 Plain Street, Marshfield, Massachusetts

*Associated Companies*
Pitman Publishing Pty Ltd, Melbourne
Pitman Publishing New Zealand Ltd, Wellington
Copp Clark Pitman, Toronto

© J-P Benqué, A Hauguel, P-L Viollet, 1982

**Library of Congress Cataloging in Publication Data**

Benqué, J.-P.
  Numerical models in environmental fluid
mechanics.

  (Engineering applications of computational
hydraulics; v. 2) (Monographs and surveys
in water resources engineering;    )
    Bibliography: p.
    1. Hydraulics—Mathematical models.
2. Atmospheric circulation—Mathematical
models.  3. Preissman, Alexander, 1916-
1. Hauguel, A. II. Viollet, P.-L. III. Title.
IV. Series. V. Series: Monographs and surveys
in water resources engineering;
TC.E5  vol. 2    627'.0724s    81-14369

ISBN 0-273-08543-3 [627'.042'0724] AACR2

**British Library Cataloguing in Publication Data**

Abbott, M. A.
  Engineering applications of computational
  hydraulics.
  Vol. 2.—(Monographs and surveys in water
  resources engineering; 6)
  1. Hydrology—Simulation methods
  2. Hydrology—Data processing
  I. Title  II. Cunge, J. A.  III. Series
  551.48'0724    GB665

  ISBN 0-273-08543-3

Filmset and printed at The Universities Press (Belfast) Ltd, and bound in Great Britain at
the Pitman Press, Bath Avon.

# Contents

# Contents to volume I

# Preface

The environment is an old problem. Since the very beginning of his existence, man has sought to protect himself against the elements. For a long time, man's knowledge of nature was limited to determining the forces which had to be taken into account so that structures would be able to resist the effects of time. In such cases, engineers were often satisfied with a very limited knowledge of the natural environment, which was usually restricted to the site where new structures were planned, and interaction with the site was not taken into account.

As the size and number of industrial installations started to increase, engineers were obliged to formulate other questions. For instance, would the very presence of the structures they created have an effect upon the natural environment because of any discharge from these structures into the environment? These new preoccupations gave rise to a new type of investigation, namely, impact studies. The idea behind such studies is essentially to try to quantify the effects of an industrial entity upon the natural environment. In order to do this, a knowledge of natural phenomena is essential. The studies to be carried out would cover vast areas, and the objective would be to understand certain mechanisms governing the environment in order to be able to predict how they might be influenced by the planned project.

In a very schematic manner, one can state that the two problems related to fluid mechanics which are most often encountered concern either the transport of certain quantities by currents (dilution of outfall; transport of sediment, spreading of oil slicks, etc.) or the determination of a pressure field or water level directly related to construction problems (water agitation in ports, determination of intake height, etc.). Although rarely an end in itself, the determination of currents is often the most important phase in mathematical models, and that is why a detailed description is presented here. The following diagram provides a partial summary of the utilization of models in the study of environmental problems by the Laboratoire National d'Hydraulique.

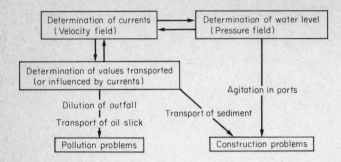

The currents and the quantities transported often interact (e.g., buoyancy of the pollutant modifying the velocity field, change in the profile of the sea-bed). As a result, there is a double arrow between the determination of the values transported and that for the velocity field.

In order to approach certain natural phenomena, one can use either on-site methods or models. On-site measurements are difficult to make, which necessarily limits their number, and they rarely make it possible to understand a phenomenon. On the other hand, they can be used to verify models which are flexible enough, so that it is possible to obtain sufficient information and consequently acquire a good understanding of the phenomena being investigated.

We have chosen to discuss some numerical models used to handle different environmental problems. Such models generally have three aspects:

(a) The analysis of the physical phenomena to be investigated and the determination of a system of equations, generally partial differential equations, to create the model.

(b) The determination of a numerical analysis algorithm which makes it possible to obtain an approximate solution to the above-mentioned equations.

(c) The coding, that is, the translation of the selected algorithm into computer language.

In the present context, an attempt will be made essentially to describe the first two aspects and to illustrate the kinds of results the different types of model which will be examined can provide. Wherever possible, measurements from natural situations or reduced-scale models will be used as a basis for comparison, so that it is possible to appreciate the validity of the model used. An effort will also be made to show which problems still present important difficulties and which are now being worked on in the context of research or development projects. Given the present state of data-processing knowledge and possibilities, there exists no general model which can be applied to all problems encountered. Individual models will be made for different classes of flow, and the aim of this book is to give an idea of the range of models used as a function of the scale and type of phenomena being investigated.

First, a distinction can be made between two major categories: the marine environment and the atmosphere. Different models have been constructed in each case, depending upon the current configuration (tide, river, wind) and the scale of the phenomena (near field, far field). This has led us to organize the material in this book into three parts, two of which are concerned with the movement of water (tidal flows, wind-generated currents on lakes, permanent flow in rivers) and the third with movement in the atmosphere.

In conclusion, we would like to mention that this work is dedicated to Dr Preissmann with deeply felt sincerity. We hope that he will excuse its form, which is not always what it might have been as a result of the limited time available.

J-P Benqué, A Hauguel and P-L Viollet
Chatou, March 1982

# Acknowledgement

This book describes several studies which were supported in part by the Service Technique Central des Ports Maritimes et des Voies Navigables and the Service des Phares et Balises et de la Navigation of the French Ministère de la Mer, and the Sous-Direction des Eaux Continentales of the French Ministère de l'Environnement.

# Part 1 Tidal flows

# 1 Introduction

Studies carried out in the past ten years by the Laboratoire National d'Hydraulique, in connection with the construction of coastal nuclear power stations, made it necessary to develop new investigative tools. In tidal flows, the influence of an outfall from a power station is limited to a strip along the coast, about 3 to 4 km wide. Little is generally known about the currents in such strips, and they are strongly influenced by the presence of the sea-bed and the coast.

Three numerical models were constructed for tidal propagation: one for the coast from Spain to Brittany; another for the English Channel; and, to link the two, a third going around Brittany. These three models each provided the boundary conditions for the regional models, which in turn made it possible to define the boundary conditions for the local models at the scale of the influence of our power stations. These nested models illustrate the principle behind our efforts, and this principle was used as a guide throughout our work. It would not have been worthwhile to use the same degree of precision for the three major tidal-propagation models as for the local models, for which a detailed description of the sea-beds and the coasts is, in fact, necessary. The consequences at the numerical level were also important. The need to use a finer grid for the local models was responsible for the fact that more sophisticated computational methods were required, especially to eliminate the time-step integration of all stability conditions involved in the spatial grid.

The experience acquired in developing tidal–current models also made it possible to approach other problems in maritime hydraulics. These are problems which are more oriented toward the investigation of surface oscillations in port structures (seiches and storm-wave agitation), and problems involving transport by currents.

This introduction is only intended to explain the procedure which led us to make up the quite varied group of computer codes presented in this first part.

Chapter 2 contains an initial presentation of the hypotheses and the development of the equations for steep shallow-water waves. This is the general context of the models for all the wave phenomena mentioned above. The various phenomena, i.e., tides, seiches and waves, are then presented along with both the physical and mathematical ramifications that have to be derived in order to construct a numerical model. Finally, the five numerical models which were developed for these problems by the Laboratoire National d'Hydraulique are presented. Wherever possible, measurements from natural situations or reduced-scale models will be used as a basis for comparison, so that it is possible to appreciate the validity of the model used.

The effort devoted to determining the currents in the vicinity of coasts is justified in Chapter 3, in which three types of problem involving transport by currents are dealt with:

(a) transport of temperature;
(b) transport and spreading of oil slicks;
(c) transport of bed sediment (drifting and the resultant bed changes).

The last is the one in which the limitations of two-dimensional models are seen, and that is why behaviour in the third dimension is introduced in Chapter 4.

# 2 Shallow-water models

## 2.1 Equations

Shallow-water waves, i.e., tides on the Continental Shelf, seiches and long waves, generally have good vertical uniformity of the horizontal components of their velocity. This property will be used to reduce this three-dimensional problem to two dimensions. In order to do this, one assumes a certain vertical behaviour for the velocities (which sets the limits to the application of the model) and then averages the various local equations over this spatial dimension.

### 2.1.1 Assumptions

The following assumptions are used for the computations:

(a) incompressible fluid;
(b) vertically uniform horizontal components of the velocity $(u, v)$ at a given time;
(c) linear vertical component of the velocity, $w$, between the elevation of the bed, $z_F$, and the elevation of the surface, $\eta$.

At the bed,

$$w(z_F) = u\frac{\partial z_F}{\partial x} + v\frac{\partial z_F}{\partial x} = w_0$$

and at the surface,

$$w(\eta) = \frac{d\eta}{dt} = \frac{\partial \eta}{\partial t} + u\frac{\partial \eta}{\partial x} + v\frac{\partial \eta}{\partial y} = w_0 + \Delta w.$$

Let

$$w_0 = u\frac{\partial z_F}{\partial x} + v\frac{\partial z_F}{\partial y}$$

(vertical component of the velocity at the bed) and

$$\Delta w = \frac{\partial h}{\partial t} + u\frac{\partial h}{\partial x} + v\frac{\partial h}{\partial y}$$

(difference in vertical velocity between the bed and the surface, $h$ being the depth of water).

Then, since $w$ is linear,

$$w(z) = w_0 + \frac{\Delta w}{h}(z - z_F).$$

It should be noted that these assumptions for the continuity equation yield the same one given by the Saint-Venant theory. In fact, by integration of the incompressibility equation over the depth,

$$\frac{\partial u}{\partial x} + \frac{\partial v}{\partial y} + \frac{\partial w}{\partial z} = 0,$$

only the vertical components of the velocity at the bed and at the surface are involved:

$$h\frac{\partial u}{\partial x} + h\frac{\partial v}{\partial y} + w(\eta) - w(z_F) = 0$$

or

$$\frac{\partial h}{\partial t} + \frac{\partial U}{\partial x} + \frac{\partial V}{\partial y} = 0, \tag{2.1}$$

where $U = uh$ and $V = vh$.

### 2.1.2 Determination of the pressure

The distribution of the vertical component of the velocity, $w(z)$, and the third momentum equation make it possible to determine the pressure, $p$. The momentum equation along $Oz$ is written as follows:

$$+\frac{1}{\rho}\frac{\partial p}{\partial z} + g + \left(\frac{\partial w}{\partial t} + u\frac{\partial w}{\partial x} + v\frac{\partial w}{\partial y} + w\frac{\partial w}{\partial z}\right) = 0$$

or

$$\frac{p}{\rho} = g(\eta - z) + \int_z^\eta \left(\frac{\partial w}{\partial t} + u\frac{\partial w}{\partial x} + v\frac{\partial w}{\partial y} + \frac{1}{2}\frac{\partial w^2}{\partial z}\right)dz.$$

If each term of the integral is computed separately, then

$$\int_z^\eta \frac{\partial w}{\partial t}dz = (\eta - z)\frac{\partial w_0}{\partial t} + \frac{\eta^2 - z^2}{2}\frac{\partial}{\partial t}\left(\frac{\Delta w}{h}\right) - (\eta - z)\frac{\partial}{\partial t}\left(z_F\frac{\Delta w}{h}\right),$$

and if the same is done for the derivatives in $x$ and $y$, then

$$\int_z^\eta \frac{1}{2}\frac{\partial w^2}{\partial z}\,dz = \frac{1}{2}(w_0+\Delta w)^2 - \frac{1}{2}\left[w_0+\frac{\Delta w}{h}(w-z_F)\right]^2$$

$$= (\eta-z)w_0\frac{\Delta w}{h}+\frac{\eta^2-z^2}{2}\frac{\Delta w^2}{h^2}-(\eta-z)z_F\frac{\Delta w^2}{h^2}.$$

As a result of the continuity equation,

$$\Delta w = -h\frac{\partial u}{\partial x}-h\frac{\partial v}{\partial y},$$

the following applies for any function $f$:

$$\frac{\partial f}{\partial t}+u\frac{\partial f}{\partial x}+v\frac{\partial f}{\partial y}+f\frac{\Delta w}{h}=\frac{1}{h}\frac{d}{dt}(fh)$$

and the pressure is expressed in the following form:

$$\frac{p}{\rho}=g(\eta-z)+\frac{\eta-z}{h}\frac{d}{dt}(hw_0-z_F\Delta w)+\frac{\eta^2-z^2}{2h}\frac{d}{dt}(\Delta w), \tag{2.2}$$

The pressure is not hydrostatic, as it is according to the Saint-Venant hypothesis. Additional terms which translate the effect of the curvature of fluid trajectories may exist.

### 2.1.3 Equations for steep shallow-water waves

In addition to the continuity equation which has already been obtained, the momentum equations must be integrated for $Ox$ and $Oy$ to obtain the equations for steep shallow-water waves. These are two-dimensional equations with three unknowns: $h$, $U$ and $V$.

Taking into account these assumptions, the momentum equations are written as

$$\frac{\partial u}{\partial t}+\frac{\partial u^2}{\partial x}+\frac{\partial uv}{\partial y}+\frac{\partial uw}{\partial z}=-\frac{1}{\rho}\frac{\partial P}{\partial x}+\nu_h\Delta_{xy}u+\frac{\partial}{\partial z}\left(\nu_z\frac{\partial u}{\partial z}\right)+fv$$

$$\frac{\partial v}{\partial t}+\frac{\partial uv}{\partial x}+\frac{\partial v^2}{\partial y}+\frac{\partial vw}{\partial z}=-\frac{1}{\rho}\frac{\partial P}{\partial y}+\nu_h\Delta_{xy}v+\frac{\partial}{\partial z}\left(\nu_z\frac{\partial v}{\partial z}\right)-fu,$$

where $f$ is the Coriolis parameter. We have assumed a distinction between the horizontal viscosity coefficient, $\nu_h$, which is assumed to be constant, and the vertical coefficient, $\nu_z$. Normally, if the profile of the horizontal components of the velocity is uniform, the latter is not involved. This entails assuming that the fluid is an ideal fluid, but this is not the case in reality and we will assume that the profile of the horizontal components of the velocity is almost uniform:

$$u(x, y, t) + u'(x, y, z, t)$$
$$v(x, y, t) + v'(x, y, z, t),$$

where

$$\int_{z_F}^{\eta} u' \, dz = \int_{z_F}^{\eta} v' \, dz = 0.$$

This will make it possible for us to show the friction stresses at the bed and at the surface. We will simply assume that this difference with respect to a uniform profile has a negligible effect upon the distribution of pressure (Eq. (2.2)) expressed in terms of the average values for $u$ and $v$. The values for the kinetic viscosity coefficients are superior to the molecular viscosity of the fluid. They take into account turbulence.

Taking into account the expression for the horizontal components of the velocity and integrating the momentum equations over the depth of water, we obtain the following if the impermeability conditions of the bed and the surface are taken into account:

$$\frac{\partial U}{\partial t} + \frac{\partial(uU)}{\partial x} + \frac{\partial(vU)}{\partial y} + \frac{\partial}{\partial x} \int_{z_F}^{\eta} u'^2 \, dz + \frac{\partial}{\partial y} \int_{z_F}^{\eta} u'v' \, dz$$

$$= -\int_{z_F}^{\eta} \frac{1}{\rho} \frac{\partial P}{\partial x} \, dz + \int_{z_F}^{\eta} \nu_h \Delta u \, dz + \left[ \nu_z \frac{\partial u'}{\partial z} \right]_{z_F}^{\eta} + fv,$$

$$\frac{\partial V}{\partial t} + \frac{\partial uV}{\partial x} + \frac{\partial vV}{\partial y} + \frac{\partial}{\partial x} \int_{z_F}^{\eta} u'v' \, dz + \frac{\partial}{\partial y} \int_{z_F}^{\eta} v'^2 \, dz$$

$$= -\int_{z_F}^{\eta} \frac{1}{\rho} \frac{\partial P}{\partial y} + \int_{z_F}^{\eta} \nu_h \Delta v + \left[ \nu_z \frac{\partial v'}{\partial z} \right]_{z_F}^{\eta} - fu.$$

The non-linearity in the Navier–Stokes equations shows the divergence of a tensor formed by the quadratic terms of the vertical variations in velocity. This dispersion tensor, which is called $\tau$, represents an additional transfer of momentum:

$$\tau = \begin{bmatrix} \dfrac{1}{h} \displaystyle\int_{z_F}^{\eta} u'^2 \, dz & \dfrac{1}{h} \displaystyle\int_{z_F}^{\eta} u'v' \, dz \\[2ex] \dfrac{1}{h} \displaystyle\int_{z_F}^{\eta} u'v' \, dz & \dfrac{1}{h} \displaystyle\int_{z_F}^{\eta} v'^2 \, dz \end{bmatrix}.$$

The system obtained has to be solved in order to know the average currents. In order to 'close' the problem, the various terms have to be linked to the average components of the velocity.

*Viscosity terms*

$$D_x = \left[ \nu_z \frac{\partial u'}{\partial z} \right]_{z_F}^{\eta} + \nu_h \int_{z_F}^{\eta} \Delta u \, dz.$$

These terms show the stresses at the bed and at the surface, as well as the exchanges in the mass due to diffusion. If the steepness terms are ignored, the computations show that

$$D_x = \nu_h \operatorname{div} (h \operatorname{grad} u) + \tau_x(\eta) + \tau_x(z_F),$$

where $\tau_x(\eta)$ is the surface stress, generally due to the wind, and $\tau_x(z_F)$ is the stress at the bed. For the latter, the classical hypothesis of Chezy will be used:

$$\tau_x(z_F) = -g \frac{u \sqrt{u^2 + v^2}}{C_S^2}.$$

The relationship is analogous for $D_y$.

*Dispersion tensor*
By analogy with Fick's law for molecular diffusion, it is assumed that the relationship between $\tau$ and the average values is of the type

$$\tau = R \operatorname{grad} u,$$

where $R$, the dispersion coefficient, will be assumed constant. The effects of dispersion are therefore included in the momentum equations by the factors having the form

$$R \operatorname{div} (h \operatorname{grad} u)$$
$$R \operatorname{div} (h \operatorname{grad} v),$$

which are analogous in form to those for diffusion. Many numerical applications in the Saint-Venant equations provided satisfactory results with coefficients $R$ of an order of magnitude much higher than that of $\nu_h$. This led us to conclude that this type of model makes it possible to include all diffusion phenomena, including those of turbulence.

*Pressure terms*
On the basis of the expression for pressure (Eq. (2.2)), it is possible to obtain these terms from the average values of $u$ and $v$. Here, as for the determination of $P$, we ignore the effects of the variation in the horizontal components of the velocity.

The following is derived from Eq. (2.2):

$$\frac{1}{\rho}\frac{\partial P}{\partial x} = g\frac{\partial \eta}{\partial x} + \frac{\eta}{h}\frac{\partial \eta}{\partial x}\frac{d}{dt}\Delta w + \frac{\eta^2 - z^2}{2h}\left(\frac{\partial}{\partial x}\frac{d}{dt}\Delta w - \frac{1}{h}\frac{d}{dt}\Delta w \frac{\partial h}{\partial x}\right)$$

$$+ \frac{1}{h}\frac{\partial \eta}{\partial x}\frac{d}{dt}(hw_0 - z_F\Delta w) + \frac{\eta - z}{h}\left[\frac{\partial}{\partial x}\left\{\frac{d}{dt}(hw_0 - z_F\Delta w)\right\}\right.$$

$$\left. - \frac{1}{h}\frac{d}{dt}(hw_0 - z_F\Delta w)\frac{\partial h}{\partial x}\right].$$

By integrating for a depth of water, the following is obtained after all calculations are completed (Hauguel 1979):

$$\int_{z_F}^{\eta}\frac{1}{\rho}\frac{\partial P}{\partial x}dz = \frac{\partial}{\partial x}\left[h^2\left(\frac{g}{2} + \frac{1}{3}\frac{d}{dt}\Delta w + \frac{1}{2}\frac{d}{dt}w_0\right)\right]$$

$$+ \left(g + \frac{1}{2}\frac{d\Delta w}{dt} + \frac{dw_0}{dt}\right)h\frac{\partial z_F}{\partial x},$$

and the analogous relationship for $y$ is

$$\int_{z_F}^{\eta}\frac{1}{\rho}\frac{\partial P}{\partial y}dz = \frac{\partial}{\partial y}\left[h^2\left(\frac{g}{2} + \frac{1}{3}\frac{d}{dt}\Delta w + \frac{1}{2}\frac{d}{dt}w_0\right)\right]$$

$$+ \left(g + \frac{1}{2}\frac{d}{dt}\Delta w + \frac{d}{dt}w_0\right)h\frac{\partial z_F}{\partial y}.$$

Let

$$\alpha = \frac{d}{dt}\Delta w = \frac{d^2h}{dt^2} \quad \text{and} \quad \beta = \frac{dw_0}{dt} = \frac{d^2 z_F}{dt^2}.$$

The equations for steep shallow-water waves then ultimately take the following form (with stresses due to the effect of the wind omitted here):

$$\frac{\partial h}{\partial t} + \frac{\partial U}{\partial x} + \frac{\partial V}{\partial y} = 0,$$

$$\frac{\partial U}{\partial t} + \frac{\partial(uU)}{\partial x} + \frac{\partial(vU)}{\partial y} + \frac{\partial}{\partial x}\left[\left(\frac{g+\beta}{2} + \frac{\alpha}{3}\right)h^2\right] = -\left(g + \beta + \frac{\alpha}{2}\right)h\frac{\partial z_F}{\partial x}$$

$$- g\frac{U\sqrt{U^2 + V^2}}{C_S^2 h^2} + R\,\text{div}\,(h\,\text{grad}\,u) + fV, \quad \left.\right\}\quad (2.3)$$

and

$$\frac{\partial V}{\partial t} + \frac{\partial(uV)}{\partial x} + \frac{\partial(vV)}{\partial y} + \frac{\partial}{\partial y}\left[\left(\frac{g+\beta}{2} + \frac{\alpha}{3}\right)h^2\right] = -\left(g + \beta + \frac{\alpha}{2}\right)h\frac{\partial z_F}{\partial x}$$

$$- g\frac{V\sqrt{U^2 + V^2}}{C_S^2 h^2} + R\,\text{div}\,(h\,\text{grad}\,v) - fU.$$

If the effect of the curvature of the fluid trajectories ($\alpha = \beta = 0$) is ignored, the classical Saint-Venant equations can be recognized here.

The presence of a variable bed ($\beta \neq 0$) is evidenced by the transformation of g into $g + \beta$, which expresses the fact that vertical acceleration, consisting of gravity and the term related to the curvature of the fluid trajectories (characterized by $\alpha$), includes a factor representing the movement over the irregularities of the bed.

It is necessary to distinguish between three different groups of terms in these equations:

(a) convection terms (particle derivatives of the fluxes), which express the effects of transport by the average current and are of a hyperbolic nature;
(b) terms of the dispersion–friction type, which express a certain spreading of momentum and are of a parabolic nature;
(c) propagation terms (pressure gradient plus continuity equation), which express the displacement of the waves by gravity as a result of the presence of the free surface, and are also of a hyperbolic nature.

We will now see that the nature of the physical phenomena involved can be quite different, according to the type of gravity wave investigated. This can be seen from the relative importance of the aforementioned groups of terms.

## 2.2 Different length scales

In dealing with waves, various scales of length are necessarily involved:

(a) the wavelength, $L$;
(b) the elevation of the surface due to the waves, $H$;
(c) the mean water depth, $d$;
(d) a horizontal length characterizing the dimensions of the area being investigated, $l$.

In the context of the models discussed below, we have assumed that the depth, $d$, is small compared with the wavelength, $L$. Depending upon the value of the other scales compared with the first two, the respective weights of each of the terms of Eqs (2.3) vary and express quite different physical phenomena. Various methods of solution, which are of necessity different, correspond to these phenomena.

### 2.2.1 Tidal flows on the Continental Shelf

It is typical that the height of such tides is very small compared with their wavelengths. On the coasts of France, the rise of the tide does not exceed

11 m, but the wavelength is of the order of 600 km. Given this property, it is generally assumed that the vertical accelerations, which are represented by $\alpha$ and $\beta$ in the system of Eq. (2.3), are negligible compared with gravity. The classical Saint-Venant equations are therefore used to create a model for tidal propagation.

To conclude the comparison of the various scales of length involved in a problem concerning tidal waves, the dimensions of the area to be investigated must be related to the wavelength. We thus distinguish three sizes of area:

(1) Large areas (general models), covering part of the Continental Shelf (English Channel, North Sea, Atlantic Continental Shelf), have dimensions of an order of magnitude equal to the length of several waves. At this scale, tidal propagation is not affected very much by the effects of the boundary and separation layers near the coasts. Exchanges of momentum due to dispersion ($R = 0$) can therefore be ignored in models of the Saint-Venant equations. The latter are consequently perfectly hyperbolic, and this very special feature can be used to solve them.

(2) Medium-sized areas (regional and local models), used to define currents closer to coasts, have dimensions of an order of magnitude ranging from one-thirtieth to several tenths of the wavelength. At this scale, the propagation of the tide (spatial differences in level over the area) is still significant, and the configuration of the coast (boundary layers, separation) becomes important. All of the terms of the Saint-Venant equations play a role, and the currents result both from tidal propagation (hyperbolic part) and the effects of separation due to the presence of the coasts (parabolic part).

(3) Small areas (detailed models), where only a very limited surface is of interest (of the order of several kilometres, e.g., ports, roads, small bays), have dimensions of several thousandths of the wavelength. At this scale, the tide is only manifested by the overall variation in the level of the surface. The propagating characteristic of the tide no longer exists, and the spatial variations in level now only result from local currents, which are in turn conditioned by the configuration of the coast. In the Saint-Venant equations, the spatial level gradient is no longer conditioned by the variation in the level in time (through the continuity equation) but by the local distribution of momentum. This property has important ramifications at the numerical level.

### 2.2.2 Seiches in ports

These are oscillations with shorter wavelengths, which are created in harbour basins by resonance. Their amplitude is very small compared with the wavelength, and it is generally assumed that the velocities which are manifested are sufficiently low as to make it possible to ignore the non-linear advection terms and the effects of viscosity throughout the entire area (convection and dispersion–friction).

The linearized Saint-Venant equations are therefore the ones to be solved in this case:

$$\frac{\partial \eta}{\partial t} + \frac{\partial (ud)}{\partial x} + \frac{\partial (vd)}{\partial y} = 0$$

$$\frac{\partial u}{\partial t} + g \frac{\partial \eta}{\partial x} = 0$$

$$\frac{\partial v}{\partial t} + g \frac{\partial \eta}{\partial y} = 0.$$

By derivation, it is possible to obtain a resolvant equation:

$$\frac{\partial^2 \eta}{\partial t^2} - \frac{\partial}{\partial x}\left(gd \frac{\partial \eta}{\partial x}\right) - \frac{\partial}{\partial y}\left(gd \frac{\partial \eta}{\partial y}\right) = 0,$$

with the impermeable boundaries

$$\frac{\partial \eta}{\partial n} = 0$$

(normal velocity zero). For a sinusoidal wave with a given frequency, $\omega$, and the complex amplitude $\zeta$ ($\eta = \zeta \exp(-i\omega t)$), the resolvant equation is written as follows:

$$\frac{\partial}{\partial x}\left(d \frac{\partial \zeta}{\partial x}\right) + \frac{\partial}{\partial y}\left(d \frac{\partial \zeta}{\partial y}\right) + \frac{\omega^2}{g} \zeta = 0, \tag{2.4}$$

with $\partial \zeta / \partial n = 0$ at the impermeable boundaries.

In the case of oscillations in ports, the difficulty results from the fact that the influence of the open sea, which is infinitely large or is at least considered as such and which simultaneously excites and is itself excited, is taken into account. If one considers the entrance to a closed port, the state which is established outside results from the superposition of the incident wave from the open sea on the wave reflected from the coast. The difference, with respect to this state, which results from opening the port produces a wave diffracted outwards by the port. The amplitude level of the oscillations in the port is established when the energy diffracted outwards is equal to the incident energy. If the frequency of excitation is close to a frequency of the port itself, the diffracted energy is lower at the same amplitude: it is transferred from one part of the port to another and only very little leaves the port. In the case of resonance, the equilibrium between the two types of energy is thus established at a high level of amplitude. The precise determination of the amplitude for resonance is only possible by means of a condition which takes into account the effects of the diffracted wave.

The wave, $f$, diffracted by the port confirms the linear Eqs (2.4) on the outside. Assuming the depth to be constant ($d = d_0$), the solution, $f$, to Eqs (2.4) for all points is expressed with the help of an integral equation on the basis of the values for $f$ and $\partial f/\partial n$ at the boundaries (theory of sources). This relationship is also valid for the limit points. It expresses a condition which establishes a relationship between the values for $f$ and those of its normal derivative $\partial f/\partial n$ at the boundary points.

To return to the superposition of the three waves (incident, reflected, diffracted outwards by the port), this relationship defines a condition at the entrance to the port (Hauguel 1978). In the case in which the open sea is schematically represented as ending at a straight coast-line and having a constant depth $d_0$, it is written as follows:

$$\zeta(M) = A - \frac{i}{2} \int_\delta H_0^{(1)}\left(\frac{\omega r}{\sqrt{gd_0}}\right) \frac{\partial \zeta}{\partial n}(P)\, dP, \tag{2.5}$$

Constant depth $d_0$

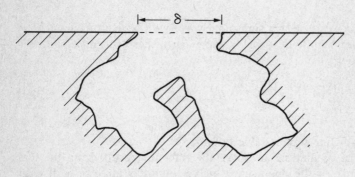

where

M, P are points at the entrance to the port, $\delta$
r    is the distance from $P$ to $M$
A    is the amplitude at the level of superposition of the incident and reflected waves in the absence of the port
i    is $\sqrt{-1}$
$H_0^{(1)}$ is a Hankel function of first space and order 0

Equation (2.5) presents the advantage of limiting the area to be investigated outside the port while at the same time taking into account the influence of the open sea as both an exciting agent (factor $A$) and an excited agent (integral over opening, $\delta$).

### 2.2.3 Storm waves in the vicinity of coasts

These are the shortest gravity waves (within the framework of models of long waves in shallow water) in terms of the length of the area investigated. This is the case in which one encounters most of the length of the wave in the area. One finds the very marked tendency of the tidal waves on the Continental Shelf to propagate, but with a more pronounced non-linear characteristic (more severe steepness). It is therefore appropriate to retain all of the terms of the Serre models (especially the vertical acceleration values $\alpha$ and $\beta$) to express this non-linear propagation. On the other hand, the effect of dispersion of momentum can be ignored (except in the vicinity of the breaking of the waves, which will not be examined here).

The equations therefore cover a very non-linear propagating characteristic and must be solved with considerable precision, and this is especially important in order to avoid masking the higher-order derivatives which appear in the complete form of the system of Eqs (2.3).

### 2.2.4 Conclusions

In dealing with the various gravity waves in coastal areas, e.g., tides, seiches and waves, the size—in terms of the wavelength—of the zone being examined expresses the degree of precision required to measure the effects of a given type of wave upon the environment. It must therefore be compatible with the choice of the model for the wave being studied (its non-linear characteristic, for example).

In studying agitation in a harbour basin or the influence upon a tidal-power station, it is the propagation of the wave which is of interest. In trying to determine where to locate an outfall, the local currents generated by this wave must be precisely determined. The variety of physical problems and phenomena involved led us to develop just as great a range of mathematical models. This was obviously imposed upon us for reasons of simplicity and economy, but also because it is never advantageous to include terms in computations when their importance in the ultimate results is negligible. Moreover, as was seen above, depending upon the physical phenomena involved, the relative importance of the operators simulating them can change completely, and all intermediate possibilities exist.

The numerical techniques developed, which are based first upon physical and then mathematical considerations, also present different levels. We will deal with the following in the order indicated:

(1) Linear propagation: seiches.
(2) Convection–dispersion–propagation: tides, with three sub-levels to be

considered as a function of the relative importance of the parabolic and hyperbolic parts:

  (a) large areas: negligible dispersion;
  (b) medium-sized areas;
  (c) small areas; filtered propagation.

(3) Very non-linear convection–propagation: waves resulting from storms.

## 2.3 Numerical solution

Historically, the first numerical approaches to hyperbolic operators were made by means of reduction to finite differences on a rectangular grid. We were not able to do otherwise. In addition, most of our models make use of this type of solution. Although this approach worked perfectly in the case of the first large-scale models, the need to obtain information in the vicinity of coasts (complex configurations), which was already partially obtained by the use of increasingly finer grids (nested models), naturally led us to look for numerical models which provided a better description of the geometry of the area. As a result, a method based upon finite elements is used in the case of seiches in ports, because the resolved operator is particularly suited for this.

For the other types of problem, we present finite-difference models with rectangular grid elements, which are the only ones which are perfectly operational at the present time, but we are trying to perfect a solution using a finite-element method which is better adapted to coastal problems, although more cumbersome and more expensive to use.

### 2.3.1 Linear propagation: seiches

It was seen above (cf. Section 2.2.2) that it is possible to obtain a resolvant equation (Eq. (2.4)) constructed on the basis of the linearized Saint-Venant equations expressed in the Fourier form:

$$\frac{\partial}{\partial x}\left(d\frac{\partial \zeta}{\partial x}\right)+\frac{\partial}{\partial y}\left(d\frac{\partial \zeta}{\partial y}\right)+\frac{\omega^2}{g}\,\zeta = 0 \tag{2.4}$$

inside the port, with $\partial \zeta/\partial n = 0$ at the impermeable boundaries, and

$$\zeta(M) = A(M)-\frac{i}{2}\int_{\delta} H_0^{(1)}\left(\frac{\omega r}{\sqrt{g d_0}}\right)\frac{\partial \zeta}{\partial n}\,(P)\,\mathrm{d}P \tag{2.5}$$

at the boundary $\delta$ open to the sea (semi-infinite with a constant depth, $d_0$).

In this case, we used the finite-element type of discretization. We chose triangular elements with a linear interpolation function for each element. If $n$ is the number of nodes of the grid inside the port and $p$ the number of nodes belonging to the open boundary, $\delta$, leading to the sea, a matrix system $(n \times n)$ can be constructed in the following manner:

(1) The weak formulation of Eq. (2.4) over the $(n-p)$ zero-base functions over $\delta$ constitutes a uniform system of $(n-p)$ equations with $n$ unknowns.
(2) The discretization of Eq. (2.5) completes the system ($p$ equations, the excitation in the right-hand side).

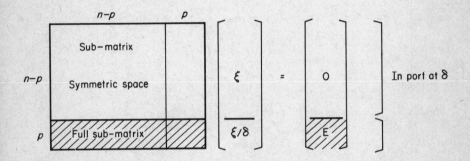

The inconvenience of this type of discretization is that it results in a dissymmetric matrix, but this is generally not serious for this type of problem. Ports are not very open to the sea, and the discretization therefore includes few points on $\delta$ and Eq. (2.5) only links the $\delta$ points and the points immediately inside (normal derivative). In addition, a sub-structure method for the entire port makes it possible to limit the size of the matrices used.

Various symmetric formulations for the same problem can be found in the literature. However, for the reasons already mentioned, we did not feel that it was essential to use them because the first way of proceeding was natural in view of the structure of our program and had yielded good results in the case of shallow-water waves.

Before using this type of solution systematically in real cases, the theoretical case of a rectangular basin with a constant depth was investigated (see Fig. 2.1). A comparison of the results obtained from calculations of theoretical and experimental situations was completely satisfactory.

Figures 2.2 and 2.3 show the grid and the results of the calculations for the reaction of the Grande Joliette basin of the Port of Marseilles to excitation by frequencies lying between 0.011 Hz ($T = 91$ s) and 0.032 Hz ($T = 31$ s).

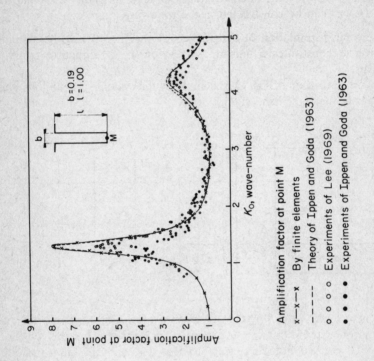

Amplification factor at point M

x—x—x    By finite elements

– – – –    Theory of Ippen and Goda (1963)

o o o o    Experiments of Lee (1969)

● ● ● ●    Experiments of Ippen and Goda (1963)

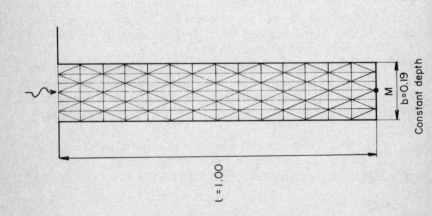

*Fig. 2.1*   Shallow-water waves in rectangular basin

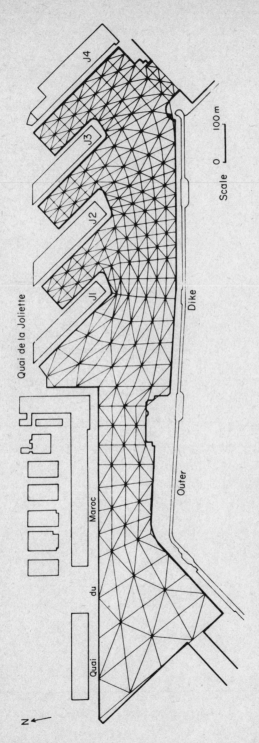

*Fig. 2.2* Seiches in Port of Marseilles—grid

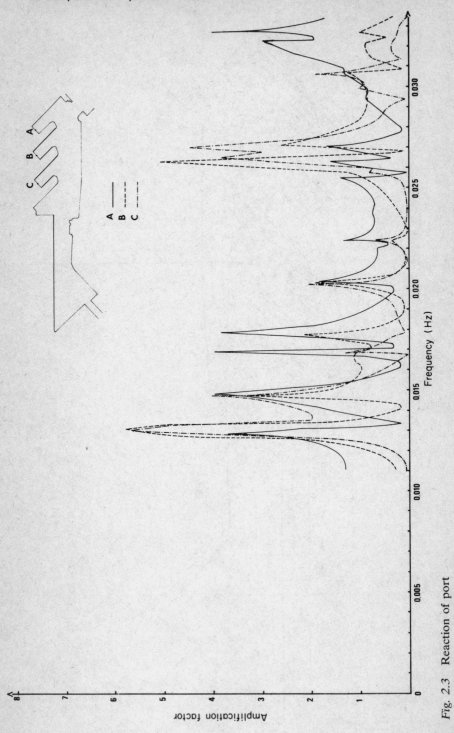

*Fig. 2.3* Reaction of port

## 2.3.2 Convection–propagation: tides over large areas

In the case of the investigation of tides on the Continental Shelf, a finite-difference model was developed. At the scale of these large models, e.g., the English Channel, discrete grid elements of the order of 10 km were chosen in order to have a reasonable number of calculation points. Given the depths involved, the stability criterion imposed by an explicit solution is not prohibitive. Moreover, the equations are purely hyperbolic in this case and can be analyzed by means of the theory of characteristics (Daubert and Graffe 1967).

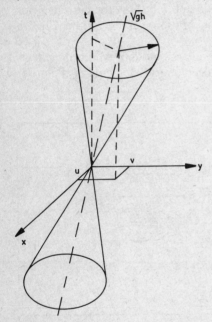

*Fig. 2.4*

This theory, involving three independent variables, was developed by Hadamard. When applied to these equations, it gives us an initial family of characteristic surfaces which at a given point envelop a cone (Fig. 2.4) with the axes $(u, v, 1)$ and a second family which envelops the extension $(u, v, 1)$. The first family corresponds to propagation (celerity $\sqrt{gh}$) and the second to convection. The intersections with the planes $t = C^{te}$ are the 'rings' seen in the water. This analysis makes it possible to draw conclusions about the boundary conditions to be used at the edges of the area:

(1) When the current enters the area with velocity $u$, there are two possibilities:

$u < \sqrt{gh}$  two conditions necessary at the boundaries;
$u > \sqrt{gh}$  three conditions necessary at the boundaries.

(2) When the current leaves:

$u < \sqrt{gh}$   one condition necessary at the boundaries;
$u > \sqrt{gh}$   no conditions necessary at the boundaries.

The theory of characteristics, the chief results of which are mentioned above, also makes it possible to construct an explicit finite-difference numerical scheme (Daubert and Graffe 1967). This numerical scheme was applied to different cases. This made it possible for us to obtain the currents of an average spring tide (coefficient of 95) for the entire coast of France exposed to the tide, by using four models, i.e., English Channel, Brittany, Atlantic, North Sea. Figures 2.5 and 2.6 show the current fields at two different tide times and the calibration curves of the English Channel model.

As was seen above, at the scale of these large models, where the effects of the boundary layer can be ignored, discrete grid elements of the order

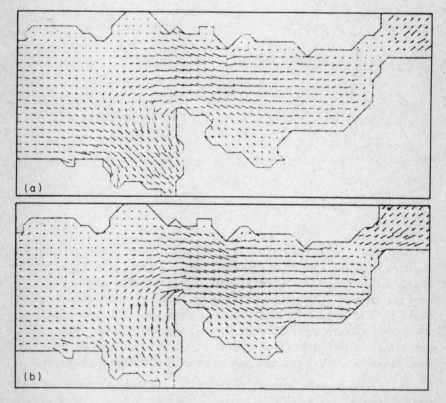

*Fig. 2.5*   Current fields of English Channel model for average spring-tide. (*a*) 4 h after high-tide at Dover; (*b*) 3 h before high-tide at Dover

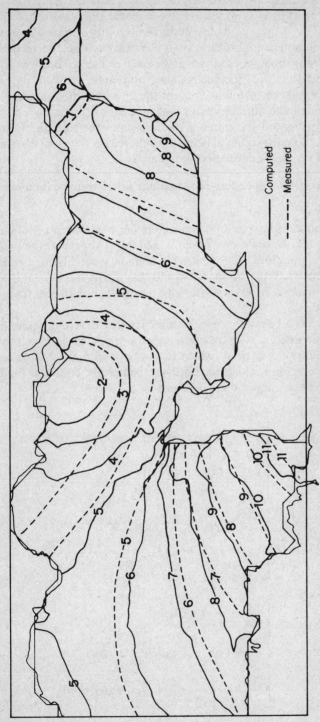

*Fig. 2.6* Results using mathematical model to determine tidal currents in the English Channel during average spring-tide with equal tide lines shown every 1 m

of 10 km were chosen in order to have a reasonable number of calculation points. Given the depths involved, the stability criterion imposed by
an explicit solution is not prohibitive in this case (200 time-steps per tide).

When investigating zones closer and closer to the coast, in which case
the area and the grid become smaller and finer respectively, it was
necessary not only to take into account the effects of the boundary layer,
but also to eliminate all restrictions with respect to the time-steps, which
would have increased the number of time-steps per tide excessively. A
new, unconditionally stable scheme was therefore developed to handle
tidal-current problems in medium-sized areas.

### 2.3.3 Convection–dispersion–propagation: tides over medium-sized areas

As mentioned already, parabolic operators (such as $R(\partial^2/\partial x^2)$) and, even
more so, hyperbolic operators (such as $\partial(uU)/\partial x$) appear in the complete
Saint-Venant equations. The necessary boundary conditions are not the
same for these two types of operator, and that is why it is advantageous to
solve the equations in several steps in accordance with the fractionary
steps method.

Each step has a physical sense. This means that different equations are
solved in succession: a convection equation (which is hyperbolic in
nature), a diffusion equation (which is parabolic in nature) and, lastly, a
propagation equation which includes the continuity equation (and as a
final step it is accorded more precision).

*Solution scheme*

Convection
$$\begin{cases} \dfrac{\partial U^*}{\partial t} + \dfrac{\partial(uU)}{\partial x} + \dfrac{\partial(vV)}{\partial y} = 0 \\[2mm] \dfrac{\partial V^*}{\partial t} + \dfrac{\partial(uV)}{\partial x} + \dfrac{\partial(vV)}{\partial y} = 0 \end{cases}$$

Diffusion
$$\begin{cases} \dfrac{\partial U^*}{\partial t} = fV + R\dfrac{\partial^2 U}{\partial x^2} + R\dfrac{\partial^2 U}{\partial y^2} \\[2mm] \dfrac{\partial V^*}{\partial t} = -fU + R\dfrac{\partial^2 V}{\partial x^2} + R\dfrac{\partial^2 V}{\partial y^2} \end{cases}$$

Propagation
$$\begin{cases} \dfrac{\partial h^*}{\partial t} + \dfrac{\partial U}{\partial x} + \dfrac{\partial V}{\partial y} = 0 \\[2mm] \dfrac{\partial U^*}{\partial t} + gh\dfrac{\partial h}{\partial x} = -gh\dfrac{\partial(z_F)}{\partial x} + (\text{friction})_x \\[2mm] \dfrac{\partial V^*}{\partial t} + gh\dfrac{\partial h}{\partial y} = -gh\dfrac{\partial(z_F)}{\partial y} + (\text{friction})_y \end{cases}$$

On the basis of this scheme, the equations are split up a second time by separating the partial derivatives in $x$ and the partial derivatives in $y$ and sweeping parallel to the corresponding directions. This yields the final scheme:

(A1) $\dfrac{\partial U^*}{\partial t} + \dfrac{\partial(uU)}{\partial x} = 0$

(A2) $\dfrac{\partial V^*}{\partial t} + \dfrac{\partial(uV)}{\partial x} = 0$

$\left.\begin{array}{r}\end{array}\right\}$ Sweeping O$x$

(A3) $\dfrac{\partial U^*}{\partial t} + \dfrac{\partial(vU)}{\partial y} = 0$

(A4) $\dfrac{\partial V^*}{\partial t} + \dfrac{\partial(vV)}{\partial y} = 0$

Sweeping O$y$ — Convection

(A5) $\dfrac{\partial U^*}{\partial t} = fV + R\dfrac{\partial^2 U}{\partial x^2}$

(A6) $\dfrac{\partial V^*}{\partial t} = +R\dfrac{\partial^2 V}{\partial x^2}$

Sweeping O$x$

(A7) $\dfrac{\partial U^*}{\partial t} = +R\dfrac{\partial^2 U}{\partial y^2}$

(A8) $\dfrac{\partial V^*}{\partial t} = -fU + R\dfrac{\partial^2 V}{\partial y^2}$

Sweeping O$y$ — Diffusion

(A9) $\dfrac{\partial h^*}{\partial t} + \dfrac{\partial U}{\partial x} = 0$

$\dfrac{\partial U^*}{\partial t} + gh\dfrac{\partial h}{\partial x} = -gh\dfrac{\partial(z_F)}{\partial x} + (\text{fric})_x$

Sweeping O$x$

(A10) $\dfrac{\partial h^*}{\partial t} + \dfrac{\partial V}{\partial y} = 0$

$\dfrac{\partial V^*}{\partial t} + gh\dfrac{\partial h}{\partial y} = -gh\dfrac{\partial(z_F)}{\partial y} + (\text{fric})_y$

Sweeping O$y$ — Propagation

The asterisk indicates the difference between intermediate variables introduced into the time-step divided by $DT$ corresponding to the solution of part of the equation.

The ten equations are solved in succession by means of different numerical methods on a single grid (finite differences, theory of characteristics). It can be demonstrated that the error made in the fractionary steps is of the first order in time.

*Method of solving convection equations*
These are Eqs (A1), (A2), (A3) and (A4). They are all of the type:

$$\frac{\partial f}{\partial t} + \frac{\partial(uf)}{\partial x} = 0.$$

They are solved by means of the explicit but unconditionally stable characteristics method (Daubert 1974).

*Method of solving diffusion equations*
These are Eqs (A5), (A6), (A7) and (A8). For example, those which correspond to sweeping in $x$ are

$$\frac{\partial U}{\partial t} = fV + R\frac{\partial^2 U}{\partial x^2}$$

$$\frac{\partial V}{\partial t} = R\frac{\partial^2 V}{\partial x^2}.$$

The implicit finite-difference scheme is used. It is solved by double sweeping.

*Method of solving propagation equations*
These are the equation pairs (A9) and (A10). For example, let us examine the pair (A9) which corresponds to sweeping in $x$:

(I) $\quad \dfrac{\partial h}{\partial t} + \dfrac{\partial U}{\partial x} = 0$

(II) $\quad \dfrac{\partial U}{\partial t} + gh\dfrac{\partial h}{\partial x} = -gh\dfrac{\partial z_F}{\partial x} + (\text{fric})_x.$

These two equations are discretized in the second order in time and space at four points of the grid $(x, t)$ and are not solved directly but are solved after linear combination:

(II) $+ C$(I)    (if the points in space are $i$ and $i-1$)

(II) $- C$(I)    (if the points in space are $i$ and $i+1$),

where $C$ is the local celerity of the waves, which makes it possible to give the two equations the same numerical weight in the solution ($C = \sqrt{gh}$).

Such a combination results in a tridiagonal matrix system in $\begin{pmatrix} U_i \\ h_i \end{pmatrix}$ solved by double sweeping, as in the case of diffusion.

*Boundary conditions*
When the equations are hyperbolic, the number of boundary conditions for each point on the boundary is given by the Hadamard theory. If one takes into account the diffusion operator, the number of boundary

conditions necessary for the problem to be properly formulated is, as far as we know, a question which has not as yet been resolved. On the basis of intuition, we assume that with either $U(uh)$ and $V(vh)$ or $h$ and the tangential velocity at the boundary, the problem is well posed.

In the case of the fractionary steps method, the determination of the boundary conditions to be imposed for each of the stages is a delicate problem. From a practical point of view, flux boundary conditions are necessary for the convection stages if the current is inward; a flux must be imposed for the entire boundary for the diffusion stages; and either the height or the normal flux is necessary for the propagation stages.

If the two components of the flux are to be assigned, e.g., $U = V = 0$, the condition of the entire step is imposed for each stage. If the height is given in place of the normal flux, it is assigned in the final stage. For the other stages, when the normal flux value at the boundary is necessary, that of the entire preceding step is used as the boundary condition.

*Sample application*
Several calculations were carried out for the English Channel using the results obtained from the model described above as boundary conditions. As an example, calculations carried out for the Brest roadstead are presented. In this case, we have measurements obtained from a scale model which allow a comparison with the results of the calculations (Figs 2.7 and 2.8).

The circulation we observe is due to the separation of the boundary layer during the flood tide. A model without viscosity cannot manifest such a phenomenon.

*Limits to use*
Although unconditionally stable, the method presented can only be used two-dimensionally in actual practice, with propagation Courant numbers under 5. With numbers above 5, the directional separation of the propagation leads to a certain degree of polarization of the results along the axes of discretization. This is very inconvenient when the area being investigated is small, because the size of the grid elements induces a restriction with respect to the time-step and leads to an excessively high number of solutions per tide.

In the case of the Brest roadstead which is presented here (where the Courant number is of the order of 3), a tide is described by approximately 1100 time-steps. This results in quite high computational costs and does not make it feasible to consider computations for much smaller areas.

In order to handle the latter, the solution method presented below was developed. The model described above, which in our nested-model procedure made it possible to solve one problem (medium-sized areas), is no longer used. The new method which was developed makes it possible

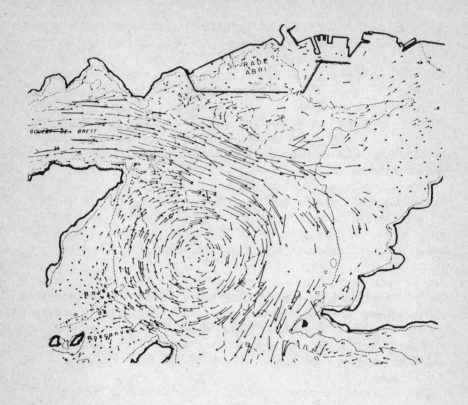

Scale model   Scales: horizontal   0 ____ 1 km

velocity   0 __ 2 m/s

*Fig. 2.7*   Brest roadstead (spring-tide coefficient 1.06). Current field 2 h before

to handle both small and medium-sized areas. Nevertheless, it seemed worthwhile to present the broad outlines because it represents an important stage in the genesis of the latter model, which is the most efficient.

### 2.3.4   Tidal propagation over small areas

In order to eliminate all polarization, a two-dimensional solution method was sought for the propagation part. In order to eliminate the source terms in this stage (for reasons which appear when the boundary conditions are written), the variable $\eta$ (elevation of the surface) is preferred to $h$, and the explicit friction terms are integrated in the diffusion stage.

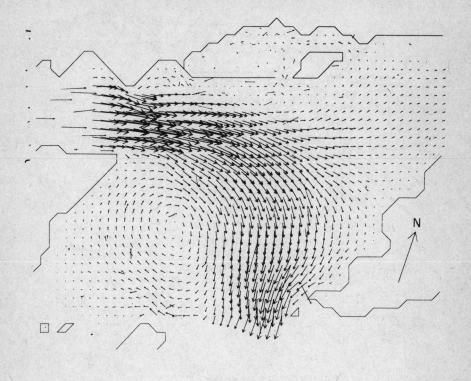

Mathematical model  Scales: horizontal

0 — 1 km

velocity  0 — 2 m/s

high-tide

Under these conditions, the propagation stage can be expressed as the solution to the following:

$$\frac{\partial \eta}{\partial t} + \frac{\partial U}{\partial x} + \frac{\partial V}{\partial y} = 0$$

$$\frac{\partial U}{\partial t} + gh\frac{\partial \eta}{\partial x} = 0$$

$$\frac{\partial V}{\partial t} + gh\frac{\partial \eta}{\partial y} = 0,$$

on the basis of the intermediate variables $U'$ and $V'$ which are obtained

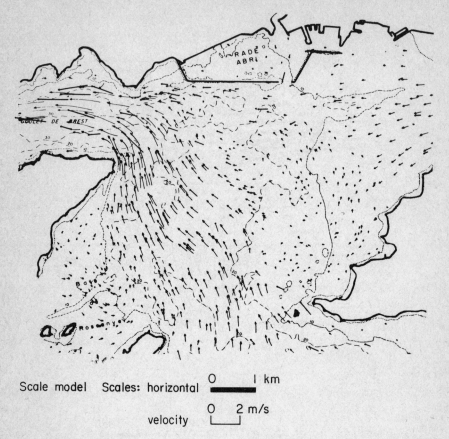

Scale model   Scales: horizontal   $\underset{\rule{0pt}{0pt}}{\overset{0\qquad\ \ \ \ \ 1\ km}{\rule{3cm}{3pt}}}$

velocity   $\underset{\rule{0pt}{0pt}}{\overset{0\quad\ 2\ m/s}{\rule{2cm}{0pt}}}$

*Fig. 2.8*   Brest roadstead (spring-tide coefficient 1.06). Current field 4 h after

by solving the convection and then the diffusion phases. Or (vector notion):

$$\frac{\eta^{n+2} - \eta^{n}}{DT} + \mathrm{div}\ \boldsymbol{U} = 0$$

$$\frac{\boldsymbol{U}^{nH} - \boldsymbol{U}'}{DT} + gh\ \mathrm{grad}\ \eta = 0.$$

By introducing an implicitness coefficient, $\alpha$ ($\alpha = 0$, explicit solution; $\alpha = 1$, implicit solution), the system is written

$$\frac{\eta^{n+1} - \eta^{n}}{DT} + \alpha\ \mathrm{div}\ \boldsymbol{U}^{n+1} + (1-\alpha)\ \mathrm{div}\ \boldsymbol{U}^{n} = 0$$

$$\frac{\boldsymbol{U}^{n+1} - \boldsymbol{U}'}{DT} + gh^{n}\alpha\ \mathrm{grad}\ \eta^{n+1} + gh^{n}(1-\alpha)\ \mathrm{grad}\ \eta^{n} = 0.$$

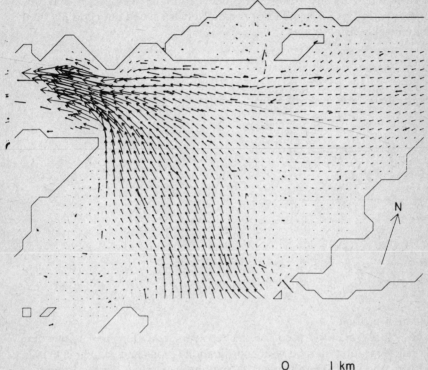

Mathematical model   Scales: horizontal $\;\underline{\quad\quad}$ 0     I km

velocity $\;\sqcup\!\!\!\!\sqcup$ 0    2 m/s

high-tide

Or, by eliminating $U^{n+1}$,

$$\frac{\eta^{n+1}}{DT^2} - \alpha^2 \operatorname{div}(gh^n \operatorname{grad} \eta^{n+1})$$

$$= \frac{\eta^n}{DT^2} - \alpha(1-\alpha)\operatorname{div}(gh^n \operatorname{grad}\eta^n) + \frac{\alpha}{DT}\operatorname{div} U' + \frac{(1-\alpha)}{DT}\operatorname{div} U^n \quad (2.6)$$

$$U^{n+1} = U' - DTgh^n[\alpha \operatorname{grad}\eta^{n+1} + (1-\alpha)\operatorname{grad}\eta^n]. \quad (2.7)$$

If the second order of discretization in space is to be retained, the form of the operators linking the flux and surface elevation variables makes it necessary to stagger the grids where each of the variables is taken. In order to retain the solution qualities of the other stages of computation, especially the convections where it is virtually indispensable to have $U$ and $V$ at the same points, only two staggered grids are retained. They are shown schematically below. The calculation of the grad $\eta$ and div $U$ operators in Eqs (2.7) and (2.6) respectively is carried out centrally on the four neighbouring points.

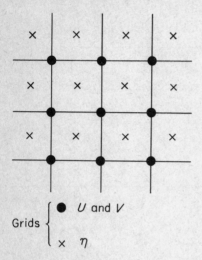

Grids $\left\{\begin{array}{l} \bullet \quad U \text{ and } V \\ \times \quad \eta \end{array}\right.$

*Solution method*

The solution method used for the resolvant equation in $\eta$ is the directional separation method with coordination (Lions and Marchouck 1975). This method has the advantage of making it possible for the program to retain a structure composed of one-dimensional solutions, but iteration is used here at the propagation stage in order to obtain the same solution in both directions. The iterative method (conjugated gradient method) leads to a very low number of iterations (10 for a Courant number of 20). Moreover, thanks to the coordination, the latter is independent of the number of discrete points.

While retaining the advantages of one-dimensional solutions at the level of the program, the solution obtained is in two-dimensional equations due to the coordination. The scheme therefore tolerates large time-steps (Courant numbers of 20 or 30) without polarization at the axes of discretization. The discretization itself quite obviously has certain effects upon the quality of the solution for such Courant numbers, but we will see that these are beneficial in terms of computing tidal currents in small areas.

*Boundary conditions*

In a case in which one wants to assign the elevation of the surface, this is done directly at the discrete points in $\eta$ and poses no problems.

At the boundaries where the fluxes are assigned (open or impermeable), a single boundary condition is necessary in this stage. In fact, the additional flow $U^{n+1} - U'$ is a gradient field which is irrotational. The assignment of a normal flux is therefore adequate. Insofar as the two components of the flux (the normal flux) have been imposed at the preceding stages of computation (dispersion), the normal derivative of the elevation of the free surface is made equal to zero in this stage (see Eq. (2.7)). This is done by means of the additional $\eta$ elevation points (outside the area covered by the flux points) which are of no physical importance but which make it possible to provide good conditions for the flux points.

*Use of the scheme with large Courant numbers*
In the case of a port with a length of 1 km and a depth of 10 m, the typical basin time (or, in other words, its own period) is of the order of 3 min and very small by comparison with the tide. In computing tidal currents, one looks for a solution for the stable state which exists once the initial parasitic fluctuations (fluctuations which result from a lack of knowledge of the initial state) are ignored.

The use of large time-steps filters out the short waves. The attractiveness of the two-dimensional solution under these conditions depends upon more than one consideration:

(a) the filter created in this manner eliminates parasitic fluctuations related to the initial conditions, which are necessarily wrong;
(b) it reduces the 'computation' costs for each tide because of the filter which results from increasing the time-step.

A detailed analysis of the curves defining the damping and the phase error of the discretization obtained for values of $\alpha$ ranging from 0.5 to 1, of the Courant number, $kp$, ranging from 0.1 to 100, and for the number of points per wavelength, $n$, ranging from 3 to 1000, shows that:

(a) the phase error does not vary much (for a given $kp$) as a function of $\alpha$ and corresponds to a shift toward the high frequencies;
(b) for a given $kp$, the most damped frequency corresponds to a description of the development of the wave for four points in time, or $4 \times kp$ points in space.

For the investigation of tidal currents, a periodic state with a period of approximately $T = 12$ h is desired. If this periodic state is analyzed in the Fourier form, it consists of the fundamental $T = 12$ h plus the harmonics with a period of $T/n$ ($n$ being whole).

Tidal phenomena (which are of astronomical origin) are sinusoidal in deep water; only on the Continental Shelf does the shallower water give rise to harmonics as a result of non-linear convection and friction terms. In fact, it can be demonstrated that the first harmonic ($T = 6$ h) is caused by non-linear convection terms and the second ($T = 4$ h) by friction. In practice, the tide has only very few important harmonics (two or three) at the degree of precision of the calculations in small areas close to the coast.

Assuming three important harmonics, the shortest important period ($T = 3$ h) is considerably longer than the time it takes for a wave to come and go in the area (3 min per 10 m of depth and 1 km of length). In other words, there is no relationship between these two phenomena. (It should be recalled that there is a non-linear influence between two frequencies $f_0 \leq f_1$ if $f_1 < 3f_0$: the non-linear quadratic terms make the frequencies $2f_0$ and $f_1 - f_0$ appear.) One can therefore filter out the high frequencies without modifying the low frequencies in the solution, which are the only ones of interest to us because they constitute the periodic solution.

For purposes of illustration, let us consider a small area, with a length of 1 km and a depth of 10 m, which is reduced to discrete grid elements of 50 m:

(1) the fundamental ($T = 12$ h) has approximately 9000 points per wavelength;
(2) the first harmonic has approximately 4500 points;
(3) the second harmonic has approximately 3000, etc.

One does not arrive at 1000 points per wavelength until the tenth harmonic.

The damping of the numerical scheme for $\alpha = 1$ and for this harmonic is a function of the Courant number. (See Table 2.1.) In other words, with a propagation Courant number of 10, the tenth harmonic, which is completely negligible for the equilibrium tide, is only dampened by a factor of 0.82. The use of high Courant numbers is therefore possible since this usually only changes harmonics beyond the tenth.

**Table 2.1**

| $kp$ | 1 | 2 | 3 | 6 | 10 | 20 | 30 | 60 | 100 |
|---|---|---|---|---|---|---|---|---|---|
| *Damping* | 0.98 | 0.96 | 0.94 | 0.88 | 0.82 | 0.67 | 0.55 | 0.33 | 0.19 |

In practice, a two-dimensional solution thus makes it possible to dispense with any criterion for the Courant number based upon the propagation. The problem then involves convections in general, which are very non-linear in small areas, and this then leads to a new criterion based upon a Courant number in convection (limit of 1). In the cases we have dealt with (see the tidal current models available for the coasts of France in Fig. 2.9), the highest Courant number for propagation is of the order of from 10 to 20.

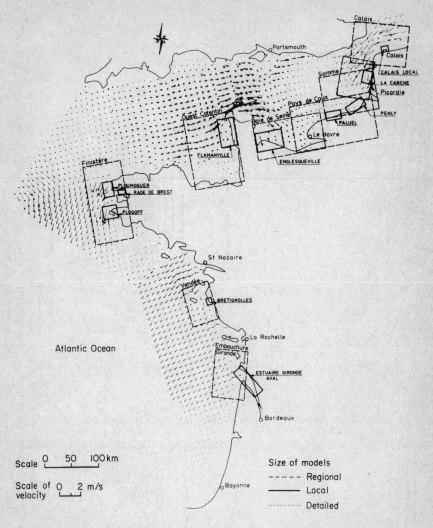

*Fig. 2.9* Tidal currents off the coast of France, 2 h after high-tide at Brest

*Sample application*
Figures 2.10, 2.11 and 2.12 present sample results obtained in the case of a detailed model for a small area of the port of Calais.

### 2.3.5 Non-linear propagation: storm waves near coasts

In this case, the complete Serre equations have to be solved. In addition to the terms already taken into account in the Saint-Venant equations,

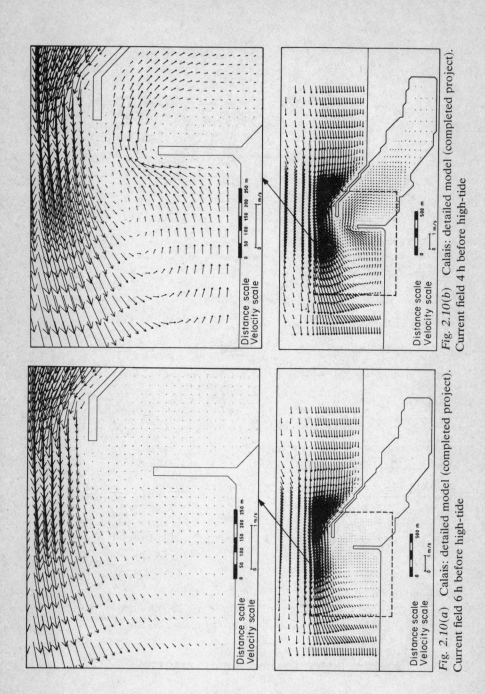

*Fig. 2.10(b)* Calais: detailed model (completed project). Current field 4 h before high-tide

*Fig. 2.10(a)* Calais: detailed model (completed project). Current field 6 h before high-tide

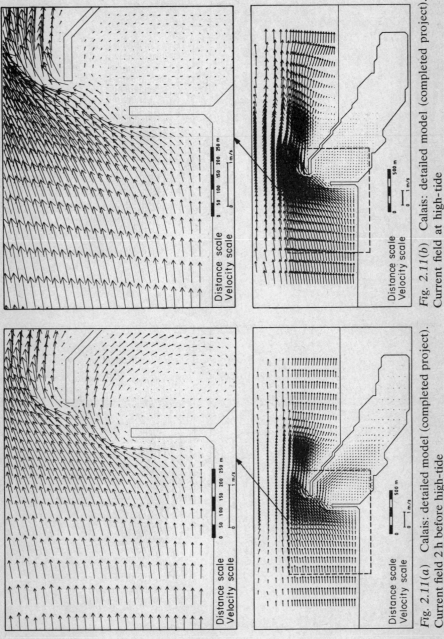

Distance scale
Velocity scale

*Fig. 2.11(b)* Calais: detailed model (completed project). Current field at high-tide

Distance scale
Velocity scale

*Fig. 2.11(a)* Calais: detailed model (completed project). Current field 2 h before high-tide

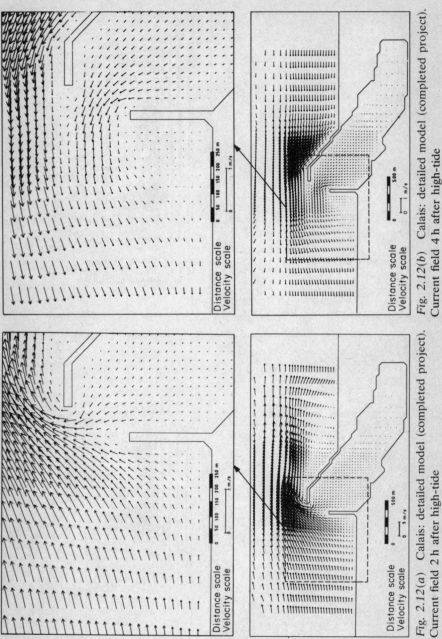

Distance scale
Velocity scale

*Fig. 2.12(a)* Calais: detailed model (completed project).
Current field 2 h after high-tide

Distance scale
Velocity scale

*Fig. 2.12(b)* Calais: detailed model (completed project).
Current field 4 h after high-tide

these equations show the second derivative in time (actually the particle derivative) of the depth of the water and the elevation of the bed.

Taking into account these terms at the second order of discretization in time results in centring the discretization of the momentum equation at the instant $nDT$ instead of $(n+\frac{1}{2})DT$. In order to make it possible for the scheme to retain the same characteristics, it is necessary to stagger the grids $U$, $V$ and $h$ in time. Moreover, it is easier to eliminate staggering the grids in space because of the necessity of determining the total derivatives of $h$. The grids retained are shown immediately below:

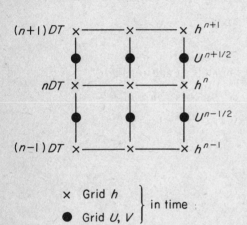

Assuming that all of the values are known up to and including $nDT$, the problem is to determine $h^{n+1}$, $U^{n+\frac{1}{2}}$ and $V^{n+\frac{1}{2}}$. Here, too, the fractionary steps technique is used. Only the 'propagation' stage was considerably modified.

*Computation of total derivatives*
The convection sub-programs are used by introducing intermediate variables, i.e., the convection of $h$. The computations are as follows, where the arrow indicates that the equation makes it possible to determine the intermediate variable $h_1^{n-1}$:

(a) Determination of $(dh/dt)^{n-\frac{1}{2}}$ by convection of $h^{n-1}$:

$$\frac{h_1^{n-1}-h^{n-1}}{DT}+u^{n-\frac{1}{2}}\frac{\partial h^{n-1}}{\partial x}=0 \rightarrow h_1^{n-1}$$

$$\frac{h_2^{n-1}-h_1^{n-1}}{DT}+v^{n-\frac{1}{2}}\frac{\partial h_1^{n-1}}{\partial y}=0 \rightarrow h_2^{n-1},$$

therefore

$$\frac{h^n - h_2^{n-1}}{DT} = \frac{h^n - h^{n-1}}{DT} - \frac{h_2^{n-1} - h_1^{n-1}}{DT} - \frac{h_1^{n-1} - h^{n-1}}{DT}$$

$$= \frac{h^n - h^{n-1}}{DT} + u^{n-\frac{1}{2}} \frac{\partial h^{n-1}}{\partial x} + v^{n-\frac{1}{2}} \frac{\partial h_1^{n-1}}{\partial y}$$

is approximately equal to $(dh/dt)^{n-\frac{1}{2}} = \dot{h}^{n-\frac{1}{2}}$.

(b) Determination of $(dh/dt)^{n+\frac{1}{2}}$ by convection of $h^n$:

$$\frac{h_1^n - h^n}{DT} + u^{n+\frac{1}{2}} \frac{\partial h^n}{\partial x} = 0 \rightarrow h_1^n$$

$$\frac{h_2^n - h_1^n}{DT} + u^{n+\frac{1}{2}} \frac{\partial h_1^n}{\partial y} = 0 \rightarrow h_2^n,$$

therefore $(h^{n+1} - h_2^n)/DT$ is approximately equal to $(dh/dt)^{n+\frac{1}{2}} = \dot{h}^{n+\frac{1}{2}}$.

(c) Determination of $(d^2h^n/dt^2) = \alpha^n$ by convection of $\dot{h}^{n-\frac{1}{2}}$:

$$\frac{\dot{h}_1^{n-\frac{1}{2}} - \dot{h}^{n-\frac{1}{2}}}{DT} + u^n \frac{\partial \dot{h}^{n-\frac{1}{2}}}{\partial x} = 0 \rightarrow \dot{h}_1^{n-\frac{1}{2}}$$

$$\frac{\dot{h}_2^{n-\frac{1}{2}} - \dot{h}_1^{n-\frac{1}{2}}}{DT} + v^n \frac{\partial \dot{h}_1^{n-\frac{1}{2}}}{\partial x} = 0 \rightarrow \dot{h}_2^{n-\frac{1}{2}},$$

therefore

$$\frac{h^{n+1}}{DT^2} - \frac{h_2^n}{DT^2} - \frac{\dot{h}_2^{n-\frac{1}{2}}}{DT} = \frac{\dot{h}^{n+\frac{1}{2}} - \dot{h}_2^{n-\frac{1}{2}}}{DT}$$

approximates $\alpha^n$.

Similar computations are made simultaneously for the elevation of the bed, $z_F$, in order to approximate $\beta_n$.

Such a procedure may seem quite cumbersome, but in fact it does not cost very much because the determination of the characteristic on which the convection is based is made only once for the different variables.

*Propagation step*

The propagation step consists of solving the following (to determine $h^{n+1}$, $U^{n+\frac{1}{2}}$):

$$\frac{h^{n+1} - h^n}{2DT} + \frac{\partial U^{n+\frac{1}{2}}}{\partial x} = -q \qquad (+q \text{ for resolvant in } y)$$

$$\frac{U^{n+\frac{1}{2}} - U_4^{n-\frac{1}{2}}}{DT} + \frac{\partial}{\partial x} \left[ \left( \frac{g + \beta^n}{2} + \frac{\alpha^n}{3} \right) \left( \frac{h^{(n+1)^2}}{4} + \frac{h^{n^2}}{2} + \frac{h^{(n-1)^2}}{4} \right) \right]$$

$$= -\left( g + \beta^n + \frac{\alpha^n}{2} \right) \left( \frac{h^{n+1}}{4} + \frac{h^n}{2} + \frac{h^{n-1}}{4} \right) \frac{\partial(z_F)}{\partial x} - g \frac{U\sqrt{U^2 + V^2}}{C_s^2 h^2}$$

with

$$\alpha^n = \frac{h^{n+1}}{DT^2} - \frac{h_2^n}{DT^2} - \frac{\dot{h}_2^{n-\frac{1}{2}}}{DT}$$

and

$$\beta^n = \frac{z_F}{DT^2} - \frac{z_{F2}^n}{DT^2} - \frac{\dot{z}_{F2}^{n-\frac{1}{2}}}{DT}$$

and $q$ as coordinator so that the solution in $h$ is the same in both directions.

The friction is explicit and therefore known. For reasons of simplification, the flux results after convection will be expressed as $\tilde{U} = U_4^{n-\frac{1}{2}}$ and the known friction as $\tau_{bed}$. All of the indices, $n-1$, $n-\frac{1}{2}$ and $n$, are known, and it is necessary to determine $h^{n+1}$ and $U^{n+\frac{1}{2}}$ at the grid nodes.

At this point, it can be pointed out that the weighting retained for the term $h^2$ ($\frac{1}{4}$ at stages $n-1$ and $n+1$ and $\frac{1}{2}$ at stage $n$) may seem surprising, but it reduces the phase error induced by the numerical scheme. As described below, the discretization in time for this stage is of the second order, and the discretization in space was also chosen at the second order:

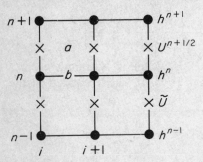

the continuity equation is centred on $a$ and the momentum equation on $b$. The following notation is used (the lower index being that for space):

$$DH_i = h_i^{n+1} - h_i^n$$

$$DU_i = U_i^{n+\frac{1}{2}} - \tilde{U}_i$$

$$\gamma_i^n = \frac{h_i^n - h_{2i}^n}{DT^2} - \frac{\dot{h}_{2i}^{n-\frac{1}{2}}}{DT};$$

in other words,

$$\alpha_i^n = \frac{DH_i}{DT^2} + \gamma_i^n$$

$$Pe_{i+1} = \frac{z_{Fi+1} - z_{Fi}}{DX}$$

The solution consists of finding $DU_i$ and $DH_i$ and checking the continuity equation (centred on $a$):

$$(a_+) \quad \frac{DH_i + DH_{i+1}}{4DT} + \frac{DU_{i+1} - DU_i}{DX} = -\frac{\tilde{U}_{i+1} - \tilde{U}_i}{DX} - \frac{q_{i+1} + q_i}{2},$$

and the momentum equation (centred on $b$):

$$(b_+) \quad \frac{DU_i + DU_{i+1}}{2DT} + \frac{1}{DX}\left[\left(\frac{g + \beta_{i+1}^n}{2} + \frac{DH_{i+1}/DT^2 + \gamma_{i+1}^n}{3}\right)\right.$$

$$\times \left(\frac{(h_{i+1}^n + DH_{i+1})^2}{4} + \frac{h_{i+1}^{n2}}{2} + \frac{h_{i+1}^{(n-1)^2}}{4}\right)$$

$$\left. - \left(\frac{g + \beta_i^n}{2} + \frac{DH_i/DT^2 + \gamma_i^n}{3}\right)\left(\frac{(h_i^n + DH_i)^2}{4} + \frac{h_i^{n2}}{2} + \frac{h_i^{(n-1)^2}}{4}\right)\right]$$

$$= \tau_{\text{bed}} - \frac{Pe_{i+1}}{2}\left[\left(g + \beta_{i+1}^n + \frac{DH_{i+1}}{2DT^2} + \frac{\gamma_{i+1}^n}{2}\right)\right.$$

$$\times \left(\frac{h_{i+1}^n + DH_{i+1}}{4} + \frac{h_{i+1}^n}{2} + \frac{h_{i+1}^{n-1}}{4}\right)$$

$$\left. + \left(g + \beta_i^n + \frac{DH_i}{2DT^2} + \frac{\gamma_i^n}{2}\right)\left(\frac{h_i^n + DH_i}{4} + \frac{h_i^n}{2} + \frac{h_i^{n-1}}{4}\right)\right].$$

The second equation is non-linear in $DH$. After it is completely expanded, it shows the terms in $DH^3$ and $DH^2$. It was linearized in the following manner:

$$DH^3 = DH \cdot DH'^2$$
$$DH^2 = DH \cdot DH',$$

where $DH'$ is either the difference obtained with respect to the preceding time-step $(h^n - h^{n-1})$ or the $DH$ obtained from the preceding step in the context of an iterative method based upon the non-linearity of the propagation. In order to obtain better results with the non-linearity, one can consider an iterative method using this $DH$ factor. After the initial computation, it is re-injected in $DH'$ and then redetermined, and so on. The method converges when $DH = DH'$. The method is expensive in terms of computation time, but it proved useful except in the case of extremely steep waves, which are described by few points. The equations $(a_+)$ and $(b_+)$ are therefore linear in $DU_i$, $DU_{i+1}$, $DH_i$ and $DH_{i+1}$. Rather than solve them in this manner, they were handled in the following manner.

By calling the equations, which are the same but which are obtained between points $i$ and $i-1$, $(a_-)$ and $(b_-)$, it is found that the same operation as for the tidal current model, i.e.,

$$(b_+) - \frac{C}{2}(a_+)$$

$$(b_-) + \frac{C}{2}(a_-)$$

but with $C = DX/DT$ this time, makes it possible to eliminate the velocities of the adjacent points ($i + 1$ and $i - 1$). Moreover, if the Courant number is rigorously equal to 1, which is in practice only possible in a linearized Saint-Venant version, the system is then interpreted directly as the discretization of the expression of the Riemann invariants over the two characteristics of the problem at point $i$.

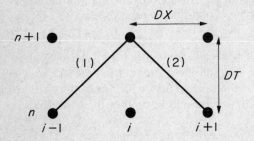

The advantage of weighting the continuity equation by the celerity is to give the same weight to each of the terms for the construction of the solution. Here, as a result of the non-linearity, it is in any case necessary to remain within a Courant number range in the neighbourhood of 1. So we chose to weight directly by using $DX/DT$, which eliminates the fluxes of the adjacent points and makes it possible to use recombination to obtain a resolvant equation in $DH$ and the explicit expression of the fluxes as a function of the new water depths.

One also obtains a resolvant equation in $DH$ as in Section 2.3.4, but with better discretization. Moreover, the coordinator, which is introduced at the level of the continuity equation, makes it possible to obtain the solution without any polarization. It can be optimized in the same manner as in Section 2.3.4.

*Boundary conditions*
At first, the influence of dispersion, the effect of which is not as clear as for tidal currents, was ignored in the calculations for storm waves. Under these conditions, we assume, as is the case for the Saint-Venant equations, that a single condition is necessary for the normal velocity when the current is outward and that two conditions are necessary when the current

is inward. This distinction is made automatically at the convection stage, in which case the nature of the solution (characteristic) only requires one limit condition unless the current is inward. We assumed that the normal derivative of the tangential velocity is zero. In order to do this, it practically suffices to assume in the organization of our numerical scheme that the value being convected is equal to that of the preceding time. When the current is inward, this is expressed by the cancellation of the spatial derivative of the convected value in the sweeping direction being considered.

At the propagation stage, the necessary boundary condition concerning the normal flow is still assumed:

(a) normal flux equal to zero for impermeable boundaries;
(b) incident wave relationship adapted to Serre equations (velocity equal to $[g + \beta + (2\alpha/3)]^{\frac{1}{2}} h^{\frac{1}{2}}$ at the point being considered) for open boundaries;
(c) interpolation between these two conditions to simulate partial reflection.

These various conditions, which were all stringently tested, all give good results, including those for the boundaries inclined with respect to the grid, where the real condition for the normal flux, which links the two flux components, can be assumed with precision as a result of the coordination used in this stage.

*Sample application*
In order to test this model with a concrete case from a previous study, the agitation established from a state of rest was calculated under the same wave conditions as those of a reduced model, namely, those of the port of Fécamp, which was investigated in our laboratory in 1970. Figure 2.13 shows the agitation pattern obtained with this reduced model for extremely severe wave conditions, i.e., a period of 7 s and a height of 5 m in the open sea (or 6 m at the entrance to the port basins as a result of swelling from propagation toward the shore). The average depth throughout the port basins is approximately 9.5 m.

The port of Fécamp opens onto the English Channel by means of an access channel bordered by two breakwaters, which damp the waves to an amplitude of the order of 1 m at the entrance to the outer harbour. Except for these two breakwaters, the basins are bordered almost exclusively by vertical quays in this variant. In addition, a zone with stronger agitation is observed in the centre of the outer harbour.

Figure 2.14 shows a perspective view of the surface computed in the basins after approximately 203 s of excitation (or 29 periods). Each line drawn represents a line in the computation grid. In this case, approximately 10 000 discrete points are necessary. At this moment, a stationary wave starts to manifest itself in the outer port and then starts to develop

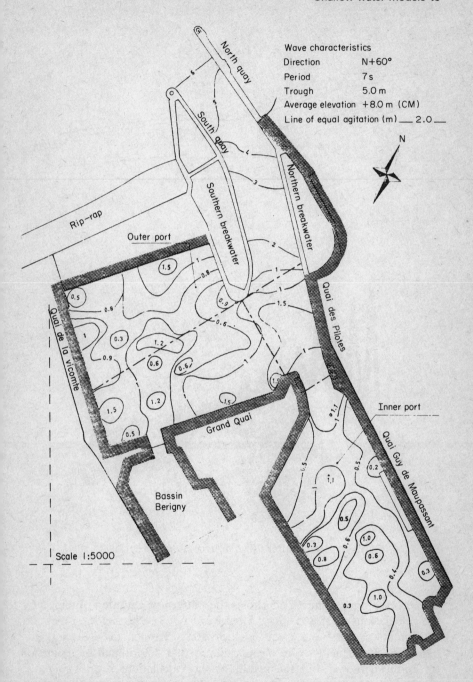

*Fig. 2.13* Agitation pattern of the reduced model of the port of Fécamp (scale of the model: 1/100)

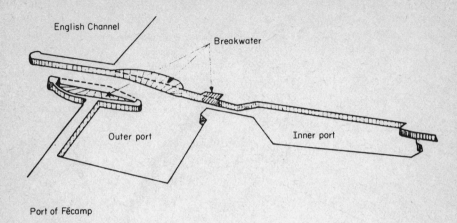

Port of Fécamp

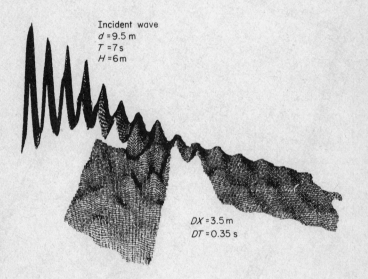

*Fig. 2.14*   Surface of water after 203 s of excitation (29 periods)

in the inner port. Figure 2.15 shows the pattern of agitation obtained by the calculations after 315 s (or 45 periods). After adjusting the reflection coefficients of the breakwaters in the access channel, the agitation obtained in the basins is quite comparable to that determined by means of the reduced model, but the results of the calculations are much more theoretical. In the same way that one measures agitation in a model, a certain smoothing effect is always introduced with respect to the theoretical case of a periodic wave which generates a stationary wave. On the

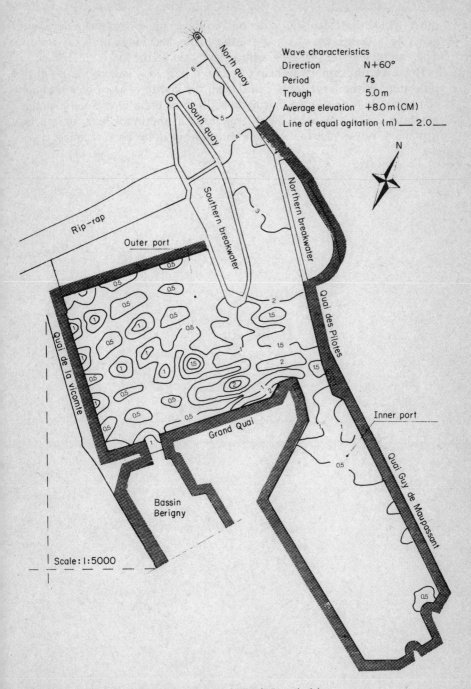

*Fig. 2.15* Agitation determined after 315 s (45 periods)

other hand, the calculations do not produce any smoothing effect and generate a stationary wave where the nodes and loops are very stable. This can be seen on Fig. 2.15, which clearly shows the loops and nodes.

However, the zone with heavy agitation perpendicular to the point of reflection on the large quay and that in the centre of the outer harbour can be easily found in the calculations. Both of them have a very similar amplitude. The somewhat weak amplitude in the inner harbour can be explained by the fact that equilibrium has not quite been reached.

# 3 Transport by currents

The effort devoted to determining currents in the vicinity of coasts with as much precision as possible is justified in this chapter. Except for very special cases, tidal current calculations, for example, were made in order to obtain a better knowledge of the dynamics of water masses and the quantities they are able to transport. We will deal with three types of transport problem amenable to the use of two-dimensional models of currents as described in the previous chapter:

(1) temperature transport: indicator characterized by its average vertical value;
(2) transport and spreading of oil slicks on the surface of the water;
(3) transport of sediment on the sea-bed (drifting) and the resultant changes in the bed.

## 3.1 Temperature problems in tidal waters

Good temperature uniformity is observed in tidal waters at all depths. Therefore, the determination of, for example, a far temperature field due to a warm outfall is a two-dimensional problem at a certain distance from the outfall. By referring to the ideas of Taylor, it can be demonstrated that the field of the average temperature with respect to depth satisfies the conservation equation:

$$\frac{\partial hT}{\partial t} + \frac{\partial}{\partial x}(uTh) + \frac{\partial}{\partial y}(vTh) = \operatorname{div} \boldsymbol{K}h \operatorname{grad} T + \frac{A}{\rho C_p}(T - T_E), \tag{3.1}$$

where

$h$      is the instantaneous height of the water at a given point
$u, v$      are the components of the average velocity with respect to the vertical movement of the tide ($h$, $u$, $v$ determined elsewhere, separate problems)

$K$ represents a tensor of the second order (dispersion) which can be computed on the basis of the non-uniformity in velocity with respect to depth and the vertical diffusion coefficient if known

$A/\rho C_p$ defines exchanges with the atmosphere

If $h$, $u$ and $v$ are obtained by means of a numerical model for tidal currents, they will confirm the continuity equation, and Eq. (3.1) will be simplified and take the form

$$\frac{\partial T}{\partial t}+u\frac{\partial T}{\partial x}+v\frac{\partial T}{\partial y}=\frac{1}{h}\operatorname{div}\boldsymbol{K}h\operatorname{grad}T+\frac{A}{\rho C_p h}\,(T-T_E). \qquad (3.2)$$

The equation is solved using the same type of finite-difference method with fractionary steps, in which the following are dealt with in succession:

convection by $u$ ⎫
convection by $v$ ⎭    explicit characteristics method
              unconditionally stable

dispersion along $x$ ⎫
dispersion along $y$ ⎭    double sweeping

From the point of view of the boundary conditions, it is assumed that the presence of a coast blocks the thermal exchanges ($\partial T/\partial n = 0$) and that the temperature at sea far away from the outfall point is the equilibrium temperature ($T = T_E$).

### 3.1.1 Practical problems in calculating the warm outfall from a power station

In practice, the problem posed by the installation of electrical power stations (5 GW) on the coast of the English Channel was to determine the temperature field during a typical tide as a result of a continuous outfall discharge of 180 m³/s of water at a temperature of 15°C (11 GW). As this discharge is mixed into the sea by tidal action, the induced temperature difference drops very quickly to 1 or 2°C. This water is then spread over a very large area (1 to 30 km²), and heat is not transferred to the atmosphere by atmospheric exchange until this stage is reached.

    The numerical model for this transfer must allow both for the introduction of the thermal energy over a small area and for the spread of this energy over a large area to be calculated with a minimum of error, because the overall thermal balance can easily be wrong by a factor of 2 as a result of the size of areas involved if special precautions are not taken. At such levels of energy, areas of the order of 20 by 30 km must be considered. For such areas with an average depth of 10 m, an average numerical error of 0.02°C per tide distorts the balance for this tide by a factor of 2, which also indicates how carefully the control balances have to be made.

In order to deal with this transfer properly, several models of different sizes (see Fig. 3.1) are necessary for finite differences using orthogonal grids, and assuming that the ratio of the length to the width of the grid elements can go up to 10. Several computational procedures are feasible to solve the effect of the introduction of the thermal energy at an outfall, of which we favour the following two:

(1) The heat (15°C) can be assigned to the outfall points, considered as the boundary, by adding a distributed flow which two-dimensionally simulates the effect of a jet of heated water injected at a rate of 180 m³/s into these and the adjacent points. In this case, experience shows that it is difficult to control the injected energy $(P = \rho C_p \Delta TQ)$. Moreover, in the case of an outfall which is not located on the coast, the outfall discharge is subjected to an additional tidal flow which can completely distort the injection.

(2) The energy from the station can be prediluted over a small area (4 or 5 grid elements) by adding an increase in the average temperature to the 4 or 5 grid elements at each time-step. At each time-step, an elementary patch is added to the desired energy. This method does not make it possible to simulate the effect of injecting a jet of water at the rate of 180 m³/s (which would be modified by a parasitic injection whose energy would be proportional to the water supplied at the outfall point multiplied by the temperature at this point). This jet effect, which is important for the very near field at the point of reversal of the current, is, in any case, quite poorly reproduced in a two-dimensional model and does not influence the far field.

Even if the equation of conservation, Eq. (3.2), is adequately solved from a numerical point of view for each of these models (which already present a certain number of numerical conservation problems), the way the models are handled can also cause errors in the calculation of the transfer of thermal energy.

One way of proceeding is to solve the various models simultaneously with a loop effect on the smaller:

(1) solution for the large area;
(2) solution for the small area after injection, with the interpolation of boundary conditions from the larger one;
(3) interpolation of the results in the larger one, etc.

This type of solution leads to a risk with respect to the conservation of energy because of the tidal fluxes crossing the boundaries of the small area. It is difficult to control perfectly the energy crossing a boundary when the temperature is assigned. In the long run, these differences can distort the overall balance.

A second way of proceeding is to solve for each of the areas separately

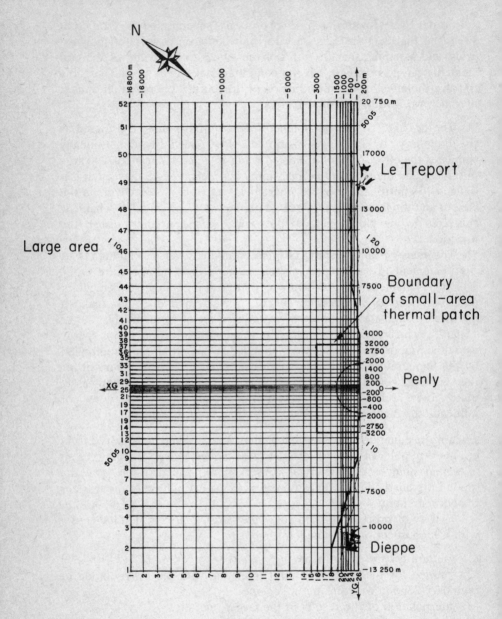

*Fig. 3.1* Mathematical model of Penly thermal area

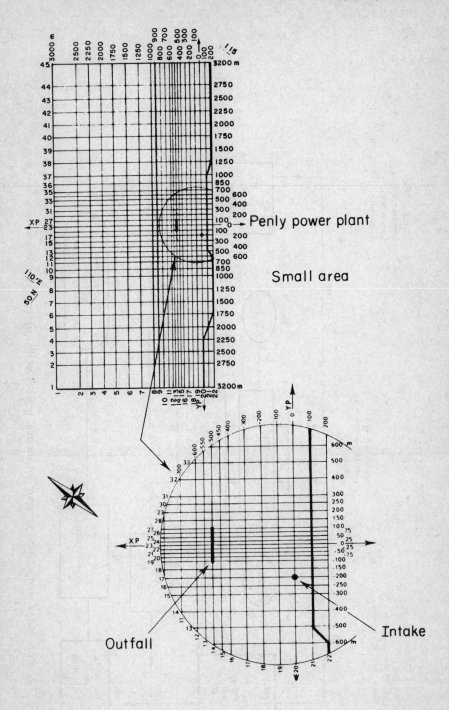

Penly power plant

Small area

Outfall

Intake

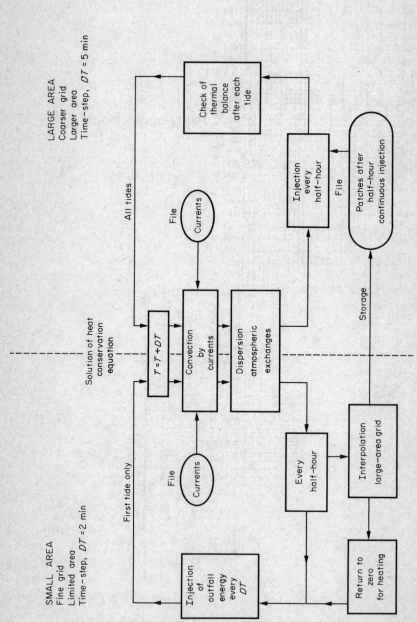

*Fig. 3.2* Principle of computation program for thermal patches in the presence of tidal currents (two areas)

(nested models used for the smaller and the larger areas) by using the linear characteristic of Eq. (3.2). The dispersion computations are carried out in the small area with the boundary conditions $T = T_E$ for a period which is sufficiently short (of the order of $\frac{1}{2}$ h) so that the heated water does not reach the boundary conditions. This makes it possible to avoid any energy cross-over at the boundary and, consequently, the problems mentioned above with respect to the overall balance. The result is then stored, the heating reset at zero, and the operation is repeated for the time interval contingent upon the tide, etc. A process diagram for this nested-model technique is shown in Fig. 3.2.

After a complete tide, patches corresponding to an initial dilution of a half-hour of injection are obtained. These are then injected into a larger model at half-hour intervals, and their convection–dispersion is determined. In the example of the grids shown, two models were adequate. The size of the model is sufficient to allow the patch to spread and thereby allow transfer to the atmosphere without having the losses at the boundaries of the model disturb the temperature field excessively.

Most of the calculations (see Fig. 3.3) were stopped after about 30 tides. At this level, equilibrium is almost achieved. Approximately 6500 TJ are stored in the area, and the temperature level is such that, of the 510 TJ injected by the station during a tide, 50 TJ (10 per cent) are still stored in the area, whereas 130 TJ (25 per cent) escape at the boundaries of the model and 330 TJ (65 per cent) go into the atmosphere. A comparison of these figures, i.e., 50 and 130 TJ, with the level of energy stored in the area, i.e., 6500 TJ, shows that the levels of heating which are reached would practically not be changed at all if the calculations were continued.

These injection techniques make it possible to handle the storage and then the thermal transfer while at the same time keeping the errors in the energy balance to a minimum. To illustrate this point with the same current field, the separation of the large and small areas made it possible to reduce the error in the energy balance for a tide from 20 to 1 per cent.

### 3.1.2 Dispersion and net drift

The integration of the local equation over the vertical shows a $(2 \times 2)$ tensor for the dispersion of the average temperature (Warluzel and Benqué 1979). These terms increase with the vertical non-uniformity of the velocities and decrease with the eddy viscosity.

In tidal waters, this tensor therefore varies in time and space. In particular, it becomes very large when the tide turns, at which point the non-uniformity of the velocities becomes largest and the turbulence weakest. If enough 'natural' measurements (velocity profiles) are available, they can be used to calculate the values. If not, it is possible to obtain

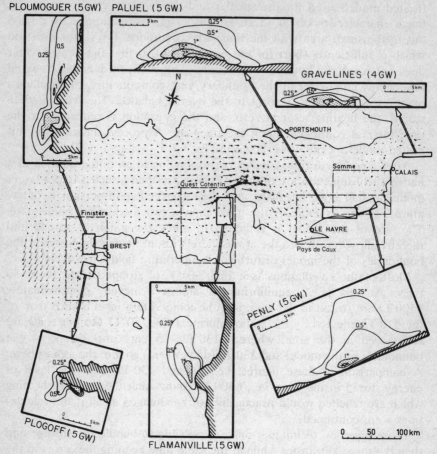

*Fig. 3.3* Thermal patches computed for planned nuclear power stations in France on the English Channel coast

conservative values (too low) by only taking into account the turbulence and the Coriolis acceleration as generators of non-uniformity and by doing this for a schematic current field (alternating flux). The more regular the geometry of the bed and the coast, e.g., a straight coast, the better the estimate is.

Given the assumptions made to obtain the dispersion tensor in the schematic case, it is possible to conclude that it is the dispersion coefficient perpendicular to the coast which is underestimated, with the probability that the approximation of the dispersion coefficient in the direction of the coast is better. For the Paluel site, an estimate of the average dispersion tensor gives rise to the following values:

$$D_{xx} = 60 \text{ m}^2/\text{s}, \qquad D_{xy} = -7 \text{ m}^2/\text{s}, \qquad D_{yy} = 2 \text{ m}^2/\text{s},$$

where $x$ is parallel to the coast. The effect of the crossed coefficient is, in the final analysis, quite negligible in this case. The diagonalization of the tensor practically does not modify the diagonal terms and causes a very small angular variation. The important effect in this tensor is the considerable distortion which exists in this case (straight coast and alternating flux) between the direction of the average flow $(60 \, \text{m}^2/\text{s})$ and the normal direction $(2 \, \text{m}^2/\text{s})$.

The numerous calculations we have carried out for the planned sites on the English Channel (Hauguel and Lepetit 1979) have shown that, more than any other parameter, the net drift (or residual circulation) of the water masses is of fundamental importance. From a hydrodynamic point of view, this notion is related to:

(a) the permanent nature of certain types of excitation in marine environments;
(b) non-linear coupling phenomena, over a long period of time, between the frequencies characterizing the tidal movements.

Drifting plays an essential role with respect to the temperature because the patch shifts slowly from one tide to the next. The quantity of heat received by a column of water will, therefore, be limited.

This drifting, which is of the order of centimetres per second, cannot be determined by the average for a tide of currents obtained by the means described above; it is of the order of magnitude of the precision of these calculations. Some attempts have been made to determine the drifting (Lomer 1978) which results from the non-linear interaction between the various waves of a tide, but it should be pointed out that actual measurements are indispensable in attempting to determine the order of magnitude for a given site.

Figure 3.4 shows the form of the thermal patch determined for Penly (a site close to Dieppe) and the average heated-surface curves as a function of the temperature for various drifting conditions. The considerable sensitivity of the results to this value is clearly shown by these curves.

## 3.2 Spreading and drifting of oil slicks

The growth in the volume of oil-tanker traffic and that in the number of offshore wells are increasing the risks of marine pollution caused by oil spills resulting from serious accidents. The sinking of the Torrey Canyon, the rupture of a well-head in the North Sea and the running aground of the Amoco Cadiz are grim examples of this trend.

In such accidents, the oil spreads on the surface of the water in the form of a layer, which may be fed by a flow—for example, from a leak in the hull of a grounded tanker. In order to prevent and deal with such pollution, it is necessary to be able to predict the behaviour and extent of

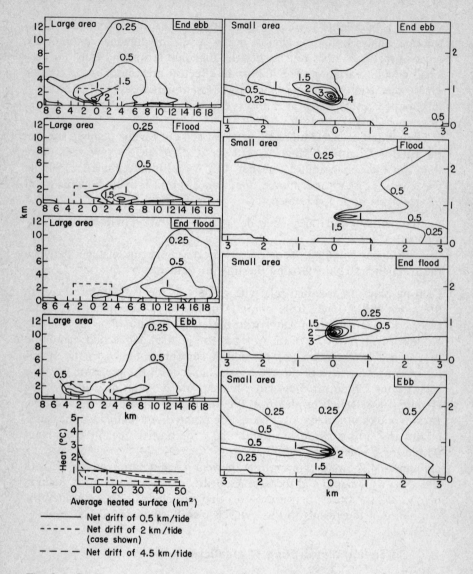

*Fig. 3.4*  Penly power station with a rated capacity of 5 GW

the layer, its shape, its thickness and the pattern of drifting if it is subjected to the effects of currents and the wind.

The various mechanisms involved in the spreading of an oil slick are very complicated (Warluzel 1978), and it is necessary to be able to use several schematic representations to deal with the various difficult problems which arise. As a result, the code presented here does not take into account all of the mechanisms involved in spreading, and it is valid only for several days after the accident has occurred. The model simulates the behaviour of an oil slick for a certain volume which is suddenly spilled or for a slick which is fed by a leak. It takes into account the characteristics of the oil and such exterior conditions as current, wind and other variables in time and space.

### 3.2.1 Formulation of equations in the gravity–viscosity regime

Only the average of the velocities throughout the thickness of the slick is important here, and it is assumed that the hydrostatic pressure is distributed. With $u$ and $v$ representing the components of the average velocity of the oil, $h$ the thickness of the slick, $\rho_p$ the density of the oil, $\varepsilon$ the relationship $(\rho_e - \rho_p)/\rho_e$ and $V_e$ and $U_e$ the components of the current, and ignoring the advection forces and surface tension, the system to be solved is written as follows (Navier–Stokes equations averaged over the thickness of the oil slick):

$$\frac{\partial h}{\partial t} + \frac{\partial uh}{\partial x} + \frac{\partial vh}{\partial y} = 0 \tag{3.3}$$

$$\rho_p \varepsilon g h \frac{\partial h}{\partial x} = \tau_{vx} + k(U_e - u) + \rho_p f h v \tag{3.4}$$

$$\rho_p \varepsilon g h \frac{\partial h}{\partial y} = \tau_{vy} + k(V_e - v) - \rho_p f h u, \tag{3.5}$$

with $k$ representing a water–oil friction coefficient. It is seen that the stress due to the wind, $\tau_v$, is equivalent to a maritime current with strength $\tau_v/k$. Equations (3.4) and (3.5) can be written with

$$\frac{\tau_v}{k} = K_v \boldsymbol{W},$$

where $\boldsymbol{W}$ is the velocity of the wind at an altitude of $10\,\text{m}$ with the components $W_x$ and $W_y$, and $K_v$ is a constant based upon experience ($\approx 0.03$).
Let

$$\rho_p \varepsilon g h \frac{\partial h}{\partial x} = k(U_e + K_v W_x - u) + \rho_p f h v \tag{3.4'}$$

and

$$\rho_p \varepsilon g h \frac{\partial h}{\partial y} = k(V_e + K_v W_y - v) - \rho_p f h v. \tag{3.5'}$$

Let

$$
\mathcal{A} \left| \begin{array}{l} A = U_e + K_v W_x = U_e + \dfrac{\tau_{vx}}{k} \\[2mm] B = V_e + K_v W_y = V_e + \dfrac{\tau_{vy}}{k} \end{array} \right. \qquad \left( \dfrac{\tau_v}{k} = 0.03 \mathbf{W} \right)
$$

and

$$
C_0 = \rho_p \frac{f}{k}.
$$

Equations (3.4) and (3.5) are then written as

$$
\rho_p \frac{\varepsilon}{k} \, gh \frac{\partial h}{\partial x} = A - u + hvC_0,
$$

$$
\rho_p \frac{\varepsilon}{k} \, gh \frac{\partial h}{\partial y} = B - v - huC_0.
$$

The following are derived from the above system:

$$
u = \frac{A + BhC_0 - \dfrac{\rho_p \varepsilon gh}{k} \left( C_0 h \dfrac{\partial h}{\partial y} + \dfrac{\partial h}{\partial x} \right)}{1 + C_0^2 h^2},
$$

$$
v = \frac{B - AhC_0 + \dfrac{\rho_p \varepsilon gh}{k} \left( C_0 h \dfrac{\partial h}{\partial x} - \dfrac{\partial h}{\partial y} \right)}{1 + C_0^2 h^2}.
$$

By introducing the two components of the velocity of the oil slick into the continuity equation, the following is obtained:

$$
\frac{\partial h}{\partial t} + \operatorname{div} \left[ \frac{h}{1 + C_0^2 h^2} \, \mathcal{A} \right] + C_0 \operatorname{rot} \left[ \frac{h^2}{1 + C_0^2 h^2} \, \mathcal{A} \right] = \operatorname{div} \left[ \frac{C_p}{1 + C_0^2 h} \operatorname{grad} h^3 \right],
$$

$$
(3.6)
$$

with

$$
C_p = \tfrac{1}{3} \rho_p \frac{\varepsilon g}{k} \qquad \left( \varepsilon = \frac{\Delta \rho}{\rho_e} \right).
$$

The expansion of the various terms of Eq. (3.6) gives rise to the convection and diffusion terms. The expansion of the terms on the left-hand side of the equation does not present any problems, but the expansion of the right-hand side of the equation is slightly more complicated. The calculations are based upon the assumption that $C_0 h^2$ is small compared with 1. This hypothesis is justified because, on the one hand, part of the Coriolis acceleration is small and on the other, it only becomes important over the long term and $h$ is therefore very small.

After carrying out the calculations, Eq. (3.6) can then be written as follows:

$$\frac{\partial h}{\partial t} + U \operatorname{grad} h = C_p \Delta h^3 - \tfrac{3}{5} C_p^2 \Delta h^5 - Z \tag{3.7}$$

with

$$U = \begin{vmatrix} \dfrac{A + 2C_0 hB - C_0^2 h^2 A}{(1 + C_0^2 h^2)^2} \\[2mm] \dfrac{B - 2C_0 hA - C_0^2 h^2 B}{(1 + C_0^2 h^2)^2} \end{vmatrix}$$

and

$$Z = \frac{h\left(\dfrac{\partial A}{\partial x} + C_0 h \dfrac{\partial B}{\partial x}\right) + h\left(\dfrac{\partial B}{\partial y} - C_0 h \dfrac{\partial A}{\partial y}\right)}{1 + C_0^2 h^2}.$$

If the Coriolis acceleration is ignored, the equation is written

$$\frac{\partial h}{\partial t} + \operatorname{div} h\mathcal{A} = C_p \Delta h^3. \tag{3.8}$$

In Eqs (3.7) and (3.8), the diffusion terms are $\Delta h^3$, $\Delta h^5$ and the transport terms $U \operatorname{grad} h$ and $Z$. They represent the spreading of the slick and its drifting resulting from the marine currents and the wind. The transport role played by both the wind and the currents on the oil slick is clearly shown in these equations.

### 3.2.2 Numerical solution and example

The algorithm for the solution of Eqs (3.7) and (3.8) is a fractionary time-steps method which we are showing, for reasons of clarity, with the simplified equation. The solution of the complete equation is only a variant, which will be dealt with later.

The area for the caclulations is defined by a grid of rectangular elements with the directions $Ox$ and $Oy$, and the following will be solved for all points, $i$, of the grid:

$$\frac{\tilde{h}_i^1 - h_i^n}{DT} = -\frac{\partial A h_i}{\partial x} \left.\right\}$$ Convection terms (Sweeping along $Ox$)

$$\frac{\tilde{h}_i^2 - \tilde{h}_i^1}{DT} = -\frac{\partial B h_i}{\partial y} \left.\right\}$$ (Sweeping along $Oy$)

$$\frac{\tilde{h}_i^3 - \tilde{h}_i^2}{DT} = C_p \frac{\partial^2 h_i^3}{\partial x^2} \left.\right\}$$ Diffusion terms (Sweeping along $Ox$)

$$\frac{h_i^{n+1} + \tilde{h}_i^3}{DT} = C_p \frac{\partial^2 h_i^3}{\partial y^2} \left.\right\}$$ (Sweeping along $Oy$),

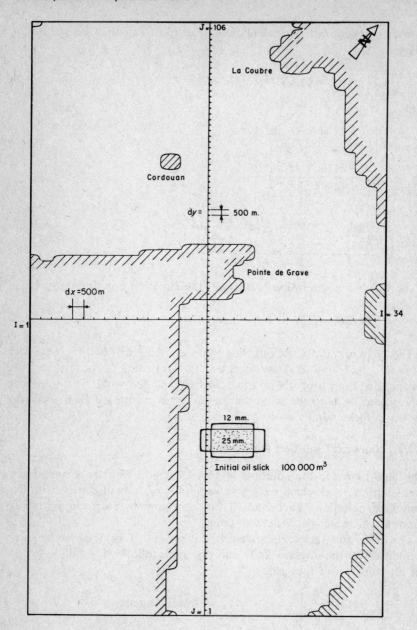

*Fig. 3.5* Size of model

$\bar{h}_1$, $\bar{h}_2$ and $\bar{h}_3$ being the values for $h$ at the intermediate time steps between $n$ and $n+1$. In the case of Eq. (3.8), the term $Z$ is subjected to an intermediate time-step after each convection stage, whereas the term $\Delta h^5$ is formulated in each stage of diffusion by means of the values for $h$ from the preceding time-step.

The code was applied to the simulation of an accident at the mouth of the Gironde, in the vicinity of the port of Verdon, where a slick of $100\,000\,\mathrm{m}^3$ was assumed to have been released instantaneously at the moment of the high-tide at Grave. The computation area and the initial location of the slick are shown in Fig. 3.5. The area within the slick is defined by an orthogonal grid consisting of elements measuring $500\,\mathrm{m}$ on each side, or by 34 and 106 points respectively along the $Ox$ and $Oy$ axes. The tidal currents were determined by previous computations. Figure 3.6 shows the state of the slick 3, 6, 9 and 12 h after the spill in the absence of wind. Figure 3.7 concerns the same calculations but also takes into account an easterly wind of $10\,\mathrm{m/s}$. It is ascertained that the slick is transported toward the coast by the currents and that considerable shearing in the latter results in a slick with a very irregular shape. The immense importance of the wind, which drives the slick in the direction of the coast, can also be ascertained.

## 3.3  Transport of sediments by drifting

In investigating changes in the sea-bed resulting from the action of currents, two important research levels can be distinguished:

(1) the determination of the physical and mechanical laws governing the transport of sediments, whereby the action of the flow upon the sediment on the bed is investigated;
(2) the investigation of the fluid as such, whereby the effect of the bed upon the flow is examined.

For the first, numerous transport formulas have been proposed. More often than not, these formulas were determined experimentally and are valid for a very particular area. They exist in two types:

(a) threshold formulas in which the sediment flow is a function of $\tau - \tau_c$, the difference between the stress at the bed and a given stress (Shields, Meyer–Peter, Muller and Larsen);
(b) formulas which provide a continuous transport value on the basis of probability computations and which are less commonly used.

Each of these types of formula offers certain advantages and disadvantages. In order to develop the drifting model presented below, we chose the Meyer–Peter formula. This is one of the most commonly used.

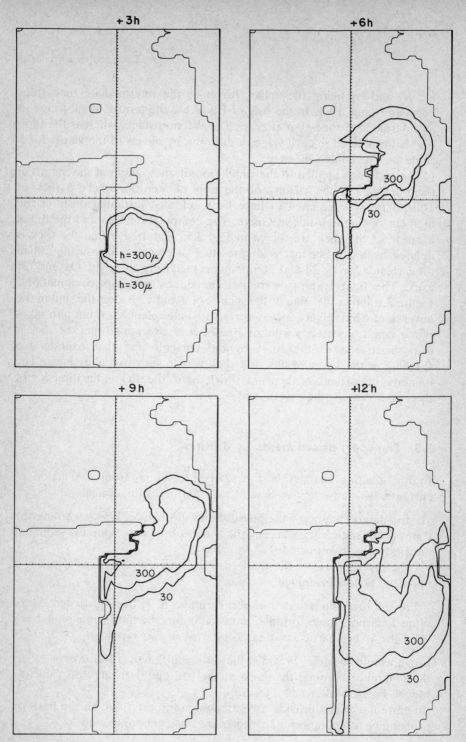

+3h

+6h

300

30

h=300μ

h=30μ

+9h

+12 h

300

30

300

30

300

30

*Fig. 3.6* Spreading without wind

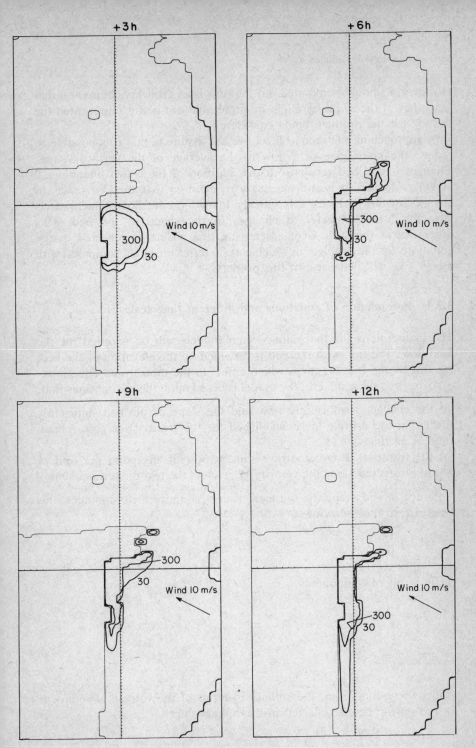

*Fig. 3.7* Spreading with wind

However, it should be pointed out that this is an arbitrary choice and that any other of the formulas might be preferable if it better represented the drifting for the problem being considered.

In approaching the second level, we are assuming that it is possible to reduce the knowledge of a flow to the average of the vertical values. Changes in the bed result from the addition of these two phenomena. Having said this, it is still necessary to mention that the bed reacts to changes in flow velocity less quickly than does the flow (which reacts virtually instantaneously) to changes in the shape of the bed. This difference in the scale of characteristic time values is reflected in the equations for the problem in which certain terms are small compared with others. We will make use of this property.

### 3.3.1 Formulation of equations and different time scales

The assumptions for the Saint-Venant models will be adopted for the fluid flow. The link with the bed is provided by the elevation of the bed, $z_F$, and by the friction stress which enters in the momentum equations.

As regards the sediment, the model is based upon the assumptions that:

(a) the change is sufficiently slow and the slope of the bed sufficiently slight that the drifting laws established for the steady-state case remain valid at all times;

(b) the transport $T$ (volumetric sediment flow at any point per unit of width) is directed along the velocity $W$, even in the two-dimensional case.

Letting $T$ and $W$ be the sediment transport and velocity modules, this gives rise to the following:

$$T = T\frac{W}{W}$$

or, in terms of components,

$$T_X = \frac{Tu}{W},$$

$$T_Y = \frac{Tv}{W}.$$

Under these conditions, the balance in terms of the volume of sediment moved on the bed is reflected in the relationship:

$$\frac{\partial z_F}{\partial t} + \frac{\partial T_x}{\partial x} + \frac{\partial T_y}{\partial y} = 0.$$

By transforming the conservation equation so that only the derivatives $u$,

$v$ and $h$ are shown:

$$\frac{\partial z_F}{\partial t} + T_{Xu}\frac{\partial u}{\partial x} + T_{Xv}\frac{\partial v}{\partial x} + T_{Xh}\frac{\partial h}{\partial x} + T_{Yu}\frac{\partial u}{\partial y} + T_{Yv}\frac{\partial v}{\partial y} + T_{Yh}\frac{\partial h}{\partial y} = 0$$

with

$$T_{Xu} = \frac{u}{W}\frac{\partial T}{\partial u} + T\frac{v^2}{W^3}, \qquad T_{Yu} = \frac{v}{W}\frac{\partial T}{\partial u} - T\frac{uv}{W^3},$$

$$T_{Xv} = \frac{u}{v}\frac{\partial T}{\partial v} - T\frac{uv}{W^3}, \qquad T_{Yv} = \frac{v}{W}\frac{\partial T}{\partial v} + T\frac{u^2}{W^3},$$

$$T_{Xh} = \frac{u}{W}\frac{\partial T}{\partial h}, \qquad\qquad T_{Yh} = \frac{v}{W}\frac{\partial T}{\partial h}.$$

$T$ is a function of $u$, $v$ and $h$ in the transport formula used (Meyer–Peter), for example:

$$T = 8\sqrt{\frac{g}{\bar\omega}}\frac{1}{\bar\omega_S - \bar\omega}(\tau - \tau_C)^{\frac{3}{2}}, \quad \text{if } \tau > \tau_C,$$

and $T = 0$ if $\tau < \tau_C$; with $\tau_C = A(\bar\omega_S - \bar\omega)D_M$, for $0.02 < A < 0.06$ (Shields), and $\tau = \bar\omega W^2/C^2$ (Chezy relationship).

The link between the hydraulic equations and the sediment equation is provided by the elevation of the bed and by the shear stress at the bed, which enters into the momentum equations, and the expression for the sediment transport (no matter what drifting formula is used).

This almost linear system is hyperbolic. It includes a propagation part which translates into two types of propagation:

(a) surface waves, namely, the long waves resulting from the Saint-Venant equations;
(b) bed waves (sand waves).

In the one-dimensional case, it is easy to express the characteristic velocities of these waves (cf. Daubert *et al.* 1966). The order of magnitude of the two velocities is very different; the surface waves propagate much more quickly. Physically, at the time scale for changes in the bed, this means that the fluid is in a state of equilibrium at any given instant. It is possible to confirm this by means of dimensional analysis, as illustrated below.

If we call $T_0$ the maximum transport of sediment which can be achieved and $H_0$ the average depth, the transport time scale is of the order of $H_0^2/T_0$. On the other hand, if $U_0$ represents a constant reference velocity for the flow, the fluid flow is $U_0H_0$. For the class of problems under investigation, it is much greater than the sediment flow: $T_0 \ll U_0H_0$.

If the elevations and distances are compared with $H_0$, $u$ and $v$ with $U_0$, and $t$ with $H_0^2/T_0$, the Saint-Venant equations are written as follows:

$$\frac{T_0}{U_0 H_0}\frac{\partial u'}{\partial t'}+u'\frac{\partial u'}{\partial x'}+v'\frac{\partial u'}{\partial y'}+\frac{gH_0}{U_0^2}\left(\frac{\partial h'}{\partial x'}+\frac{\partial \xi}{\partial x'}\right)=\alpha_x$$

$$\frac{T_0}{U_0 H_0}\frac{\partial v'}{\partial t'}+u'\frac{\partial v'}{\partial x'}+v'\frac{\partial v'}{\partial y'}+\frac{gH_0}{U_0^2}\left(\frac{\partial h'}{\partial y'}+\frac{\partial \xi}{\partial y'}\right)=\alpha_y$$

$$\frac{T_0}{U_0 H_0}\frac{\partial h'}{\partial t'}+u\frac{\partial h'}{\partial x'}+v\frac{\partial h'}{\partial y'}+h'\frac{\partial u'}{\partial x'}+h\frac{\partial v'}{\partial y'}=0$$

where the primed letters are dimensionless variables. Because of the condition $T_0 \ll U_0 H_0$, it is seen that the time derivatives can be ignored in these equations. As a result, if it is assumed that the *flow at the boundaries remains constant*, the fluid flow can be represented by the steady-state equations as an initial approximation. This hypothesis is used in the model.

### 3.3.2 Simplifying assumptions

The aim of this model is to reproduce the interaction between the bed and the flow as accurately as possible. In particular, the aim is to find the means to determine deviations in the current which occur during changes in the bed. In order to do this, it is necessary to use the fluid equations.

It is impossible to consider solving the equations completely. The dynamic equations for the fluid are too complex and their solution too expensive because of the degree of precision with which the flow can be described, which is much higher than that which exists for the sediment transport mechanism (empirical laws). As far as the dynamics of the fluid are concerned, it is assumed that the elevation of the free surface, $\eta$, and the viscosity forces are independent of this development because of the slowness of the change in the bed. This limits the problem to small disturbances.

If one thinks in terms of disturbances indexed (1), then

$$h = h_0 - \xi_s,$$

with $\eta$ varying during the tide but independent of $\xi_s$, the variation in the elevation of the bed, and

$$\text{rot } \boldsymbol{W}_1 = 0,$$

irrotational movement in disturbances.

The above replace the momentum equations. As far as the continuity equation is concerned, it is written as follows:

$$\frac{\partial h}{\partial t}+\text{div}\,(h\boldsymbol{W})=0$$

or

$$\frac{\partial h_0}{\partial t} - \frac{\partial \xi_s}{\partial t} + \text{div}\left[(h_0 - \xi_s)\boldsymbol{W}\right] = 0.$$

At this level, the difference in scale between the fluid flux, $h\boldsymbol{W}$, and the sediment transport, $\boldsymbol{T}$, shown for the steady-state case in Section 3.3.1 is used. The same property is found here; if the continuity equation written in this manner is compared with the sediment conservation equation, then

$$\frac{\partial \xi_s}{\partial t} + \text{div}\,\boldsymbol{T} = 0.$$

The difference in scale, $T \ll hW$, makes it possible to ignore $\partial \xi_s/\partial t$ in the continuity equation:

$$-\frac{\partial \xi_s}{\partial t} = \text{div}\,\boldsymbol{T} \ll \text{div}\,h\boldsymbol{W}.$$

This is therefore reduced to

$$\frac{\partial h_0}{\partial t} + \text{div}\left[(h_0 - \xi_s)\boldsymbol{W}\right] = 0.$$

For the rest of the computations, it is then convenient to introduce the velocity disturbances and to write $\boldsymbol{W}$ in the following form:

$$\boldsymbol{W}\begin{cases} u = u_0 + u_0 \dfrac{\xi_s}{h_0 - \xi_s} + \tilde{u}_1 \\[2mm] v = v_0 + v_0 \dfrac{\xi_s}{h_0 - \xi_s} + \tilde{v}_1, \end{cases}$$

where $u_0$, $v_0$ and $h_0$ are periodic and $\xi_s$, $\tilde{u}_1$ and $\tilde{v}_1$ change from one tide to another. The continuity equation is therefore written as follows:

$$\frac{\partial h_0}{\partial t} + \frac{\partial}{\partial x}\left[\left(u_0 + u_0 \frac{\xi_s}{h_0 - \xi_s} + \tilde{u}_1\right)(h_0 - \xi_s)\right]$$
$$+ \frac{\partial}{\partial y}\left[\left(v_0 + v_0 \frac{\xi_s}{h_0 - \xi_s} + \tilde{v}_1\right)(h_0 - \xi_s)\right] = 0$$

or, since $u_0$, $v_0$ and $h_0$ satisfy the continuity equation at each instant of the initial tide,

$$\frac{\partial}{\partial x}\left[\tilde{u}_1(h_0 - \xi_s)\right] + \frac{\partial}{\partial y}\left[\tilde{v}_1(h_0 - \xi_s)\right] = 0.$$

If the current function is introduced, then

$$\underbrace{\tilde{u}_1(h_0 - \xi_s)}_{h} = \frac{\partial \Psi}{\partial y} \qquad \underbrace{\tilde{v}_1(h_0 - \xi_s)}_{h} = -\frac{\partial \Psi}{\partial x}.$$

It must satisfy the relationship

$$\Delta\Psi = -h \operatorname{rot}(\tilde{\boldsymbol{W}}_1) + \tilde{u}_1 \frac{\partial h}{\partial y} - \tilde{v}_1 \frac{\partial h}{\partial x}.$$

Given the assumption with respect to the dynamics of the disturbances, the vorticity of $\tilde{\boldsymbol{W}}_1$ is the opposite to that of the field $(u_0\xi_s/h, v_0\xi_s/h)$, and the total vorticity is zero. The model therefore shows two types of disturbance:

(1) the field $\boldsymbol{W}_0\xi_s/h$, the variation in the velocity due to the conservation of the flux in the sense of the initial flow;
(2) the field $\tilde{\boldsymbol{W}}_1$, which characterizes the deviation in the flow and is expressed on the basis of the slope of the bed.

### 3.3.3 Solution method

Since the initial current field, $\boldsymbol{W}_0$, is given (computation, model or measurement), the equations of the problem are as follows.

For the fluid:

$$\left.\begin{array}{l} u = u_0 + u_0 \dfrac{\xi_s}{h} + \overbrace{\dfrac{1}{h}\dfrac{\partial\Psi}{\partial y}}^{\tilde{u}_1} \\[3mm] v = v_0 + v_0 \dfrac{\xi_s}{h} - \underbrace{\dfrac{1}{h}\dfrac{\partial\Psi}{\partial x}}_{\tilde{v}_1} \end{array}\right\} \tag{3.9}$$

with $h = h_0 - \xi_s$ and $\psi$ satisfying

$$\Delta\Psi = +h\left[\frac{\partial}{\partial x}\left(v_0\frac{\xi_s}{h}\right) - \frac{\partial}{\partial y}\left(u_0\frac{\xi_s}{h}\right)\right] + \tilde{u}_1\frac{\partial h}{\partial y} - \tilde{v}_1\frac{\partial h}{\partial x}. \tag{3.9'}$$

In these two relationships, $u_0$, $v_0$ and $h_0$ are periodic (initial tide), and $\xi_s$, $u_1$ and $v_1$, the unknowns in the problem, change in time and from one tide to another.

For the sea-bed (with $W$ being replaced by its expression in the conservation equation):

$$\frac{\partial\xi_s}{\partial t} + C\left(\frac{u}{W}\frac{\partial\xi_s}{\partial x} + \frac{v}{W}\frac{\partial\xi_s}{\partial y}\right) = -T_{X_u}\left[\frac{\partial}{\partial x}(u_0 + \tilde{u}_1) + \xi_s\frac{\partial}{\partial x}\left(\frac{u_0}{h_0}\right)\right]$$

$$-T_{X_v}\left[\frac{\partial}{\partial x}(v_0 + \tilde{v}_1) + \xi_s\frac{\partial}{\partial x}\left(\frac{v_0}{h_0}\right)\right] - T_{Y_u}\left[\frac{\partial}{\partial y}(u_0 + \tilde{u}_1) + \xi_s\frac{\partial}{\partial y}\left(\frac{u_0}{h_0}\right)\right]$$

$$-T_{Y_v}\left[\frac{\partial}{\partial y}(v_0 + \tilde{v}_1) + \xi_s\frac{\partial}{\partial y}\left(\frac{v_0}{h_0}\right)\right] - T_{X_h}\frac{\partial h_0}{\partial x} - T_{Y_h}\frac{\partial h_0}{\partial y} \tag{3.10}$$

with

$$C = \frac{1}{h}\left( u_0 \frac{\partial T}{\partial u} + v_0 \frac{\partial T}{\partial v} - h_0 \frac{\partial T}{\partial h} \right), \qquad u_0, v_0 \text{ periodic}$$

and

$$T_{X_u} = \frac{\partial}{\partial u}\left( \frac{u}{W} T \right), \qquad T_{X_v} = \frac{\partial}{\partial v}\left( \frac{u}{W} T \right), \qquad T_{X_h} = \frac{u}{W} \frac{\partial T}{\partial h},$$

$$T_{Y_u} = \frac{\partial}{\partial u}\left( \frac{v}{W} T \right), \qquad T_{Y_u} = \frac{\partial}{\partial y}\left( \frac{v}{W} T \right), \qquad T_{Y_h} = \frac{\partial T}{\partial h}.$$

Equation (3.10) expresses propagation with deformation due to the second member (source terms); it propagates the sand waves.

A finite-difference numerical scheme is used. The two dimensions in space and the time dimension are discretized into regular grids with the steps $DX$, $DY$ and $DT$. The grid in $\Psi$ is off-centre with respect to the grid in $u$, $v$ and $\xi$. The initial periodic flow is given by $u_0$, $v_0$ and $h_0$ (by computation, model or measurement). At any instant $n$, the following are available at the nodes: $i$, $j$ of $\xi_s^n$, $h^n$ $(= h_0 - \xi_s^n)$, $\bar{u}_1^n$, $\bar{v}_1^n$.

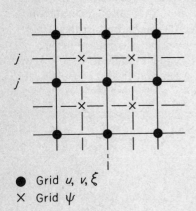

● Grid $u$, $v$, $\xi$
✕ Grid $\psi$

The computations are made in two phases:

(1) Determination of the sediment height at the instant $(n+1)$: $\xi_s^{n+1}$. Equation (3.10) is solved in fractionary space-steps by the characteristics method. In order to do this, the source terms and the celerity ($Cu/W$, $Cv/W$) are explicit (expressed at the instant $n$), and $u_0$, $v_0$ and $h_0$ are taken at the instant corresponding to the tide.

(2) Determination of the velocity at the instant $(n+1)$. Thanks to the resolvant in $\Psi$ (Eq. (3.9')), it is possible to compute $\bar{u}_1^{n+1} \bar{v}_1^{n+1}$. An iterative method with over-relaxation was chosen for this. The factors $\bar{u}_1$ and $\bar{v}_1$ which are involved in the second member are formulated, whereas

$u_0$, $v_0$ and $h_0$ are taken at the instant corresponding to the tide. If it is assumed that the bed is not disturbed at the boundaries, the velocity is not disturbed at the boundaries, and the condition at $\Psi$ is a normal zero-derivative condition.

### 3.3.4  Sample application

Figures 3.8, 3.9 and 3.10 show an application of the model in the case of changes in the banks and channels outside the port of Calais. Figures 3.8 and 3.9 show the current field used for the computations (at low and high-tide), and Fig. 3.10 shows the changes in the bed for 3474 tides (somewhat less than 5 years).

Although the general tendencies (displacement of the sand-bars to the west) conform to the changes observed in nature in recent years, overall smoothing of the sea-bed profile is observed.

In this particular case, we are of the opinion that this is not the result of damping in the change model, because the cause of this smoothing comes directly from the field of stresses at the bed as a result of the average currents. It is seen clearly in Figs 3.8 and 3.9 that there are significant deviations from the average current because of the presence of the banks and channels. It is reasonable to assume that they also generate quite significant vertical current deviation. Under these conditions, the stresses at the bed are not in the direction of the average current.

In this particular case, the necessity for better models to describe the behaviour in the third dimension can be seen, and this is especially the case in the presence of banks and channels.

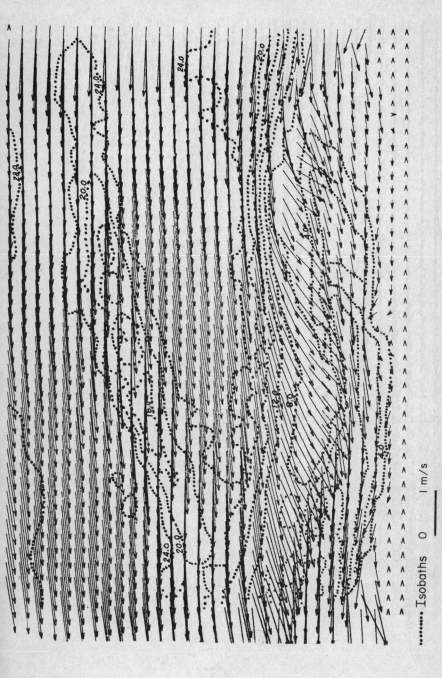

*Fig. 3.8*  Calais: velocity field at low-tide. Scale: 1/77 250

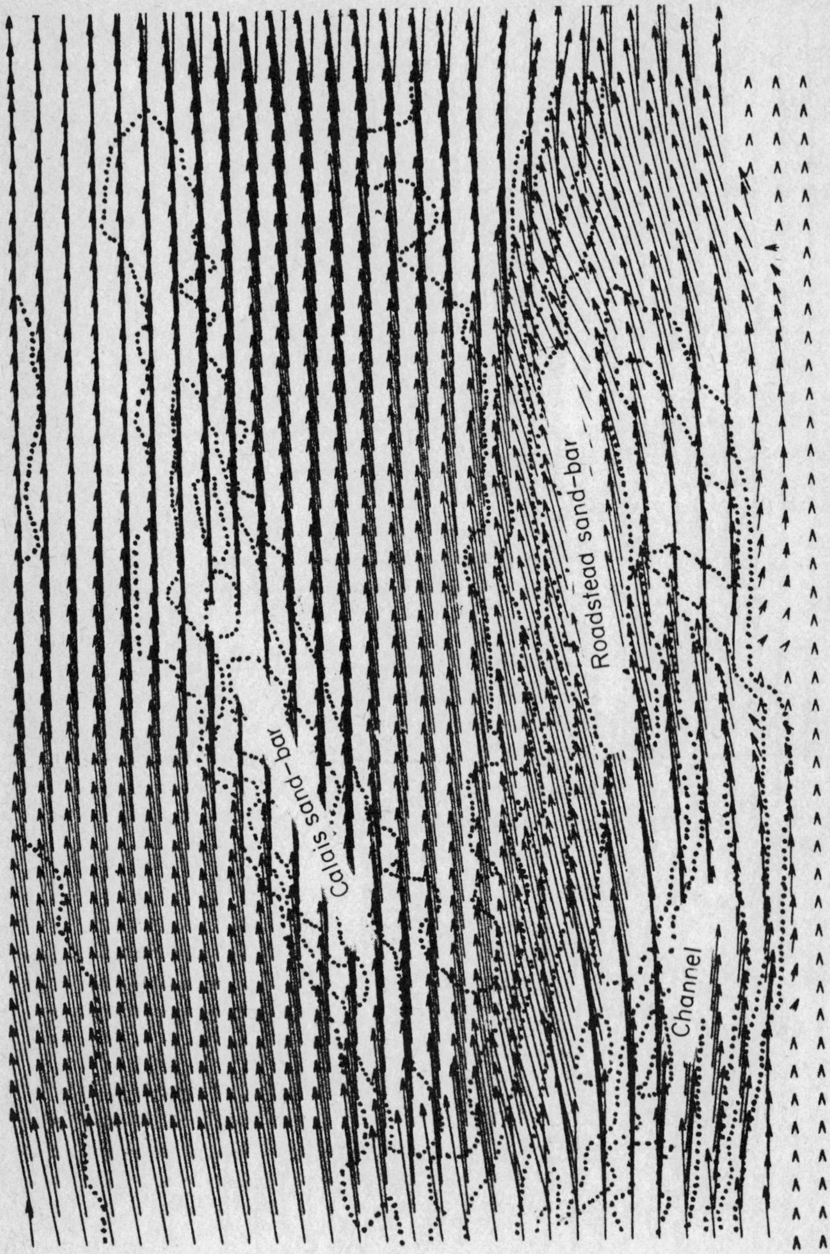

Calais sand-bar

Roadstead sand-bar

Channel

0    1 m/s    *Fig. 3.9*   Calais: velocity field at high-tide. Scale: 1/77 250

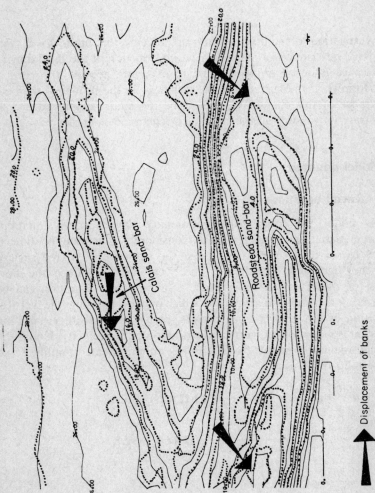

Calais sand-bar

Roadstead sand-bar

Displacement of banks

.......... Initial isobaths

*Fig. 3.10* Calais: level lines after 3474 tides. Scale: 1/146 300

# 4 Introduction of third dimension

The investigation of sediment transport reveals the limits to a two-dimensional description of currents. The introduction of the third dimension in space is necessary to be able to take into account the vertical non-uniformity of the current due to variations in the profile of the bed. The purpose of this chapter is to describe the model employed and to demonstrate its validity on the basis of a schematic example.

## 4.1 Model adopted

### 4.1.1 General equations

For this model, the complete non-stationary Navier–Stokes equations with three spatial variables are used. Considerable computation time is required to solve these equations, and the presence of a free surface makes the algorithm considerably more complicated. Since the flow remains for the most part horizontal, a simplifying assumption can be introduced: pressure is hydrostatic, which means ignoring the vertical acceleration of the fluid compared with gravity. On the other hand, no assumption is made for the vertical distribution of the velocity. Under the foregoing assumptions, the Navier–Stokes equations are simplified and take the following form:

$$\frac{\partial u}{\partial t} + u\frac{\partial u}{\partial x} + v\frac{\partial u}{\partial y} + w\frac{\partial u}{\partial z} = -\frac{1}{\rho}\frac{\partial p}{\partial x} - 2(\mathbf{\Omega} \times \mathbf{U})_x + \nu\Delta u$$

$$\frac{\partial v}{\partial t} + u\frac{\partial v}{\partial x} + v\frac{\partial v}{\partial y} + w\frac{\partial v}{\partial z} = -\frac{1}{\rho}\frac{\partial p}{\partial y} - 2(\mathbf{\Omega} \times \mathbf{U})_y + \nu\Delta v$$

$$0 = -\frac{1}{\rho}\frac{\partial p}{\partial z} - g$$

$$\frac{\partial u}{\partial x} + \frac{\partial v}{\partial y} + \frac{\partial w}{\partial z} = 0$$

where

| | |
|---|---|
| $U$ | is the velocity field |
| $u, v, w$ | are the velocity components |
| $p$ | is the pressure field |
| $\Omega$ | is the Earth's rotation vector |
| $g$ | is the gravitational acceleration |
| $\rho$ | is the density |
| $\nu$ | is the viscosity of the fluid |

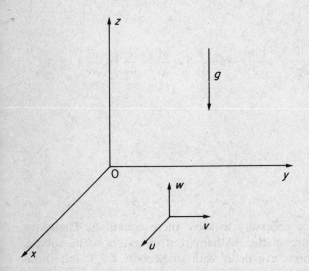

In these equations, the velocity is considered to be instantaneous and the flow very turbulent, and only the average values in terms of probability are of interest. Letting $G'$ be the fluctuation of any given value $G$ (velocity, pressure, etc.) with respect to its average $\bar{G}$, the following system of equations is obtained for the average values:

$$\frac{\partial \bar{u}}{\partial t} + \bar{u}\frac{\partial \bar{u}}{\partial x} + \bar{v}\frac{\partial \bar{u}}{\partial y} + \bar{w}\frac{\partial \bar{u}}{\partial z} = -\frac{1}{\rho}\frac{\partial \bar{p}}{\partial x} - 2(\mathbf{\Omega} \times \bar{U})_x - \frac{\partial \overline{u'^2}}{\partial x} - \frac{\partial \overline{u'v'}}{\partial y} - \frac{\partial \overline{u'w'}}{\partial z}$$

$$\frac{\partial \bar{v}}{\partial t} + \bar{u}\frac{\partial \bar{v}}{\partial x} + \bar{v}\frac{\partial \bar{v}}{\partial y} + \bar{w}\frac{\partial \bar{v}}{\partial z} = -\frac{1}{\rho}\frac{\partial \bar{p}}{\partial y} - 2(\mathbf{\Omega} \times \bar{U})_y - \frac{\partial \overline{u'v'}}{\partial x} - \frac{\partial \overline{v'^2}}{\partial y} - \frac{\partial \overline{v'w'}}{\partial z}$$

$$0 = -\frac{1}{\rho}\frac{\partial \bar{p}}{\partial z} - g$$

$$\frac{\partial \bar{u}}{\partial x} + \frac{\partial \bar{v}}{\partial y} + \frac{\partial \bar{w}}{\partial z} = 0.$$

The classical terms of correlation are seen to appear. In order to complete the model, they must be related to the average values.

It was decided to simulate the terms which represent the turbulent fluxes of momentum by turbulent diffusion coefficients. If a distinction is made between vertical and horizontal exchanges in the simulation, $\nu_z$ and $\nu_h$ represent the vertical and horizontal eddy diffusivities, and the equations are written

$$\frac{\partial \bar{u}}{\partial t} + \bar{u}\frac{\partial \bar{u}}{\partial x} + \bar{v}\frac{\partial \bar{u}}{\partial y} + \bar{w}\frac{\partial \bar{u}}{\partial z} = -\frac{1}{\rho}\frac{\partial \bar{p}}{\partial x} + f\bar{v} + \frac{\partial}{\partial x}\left(\nu_h \frac{\partial \bar{u}}{\partial x}\right)$$

$$+ \frac{\partial}{\partial y}\left(\nu_h \frac{\partial \bar{u}}{\partial y}\right) + \frac{\partial}{\partial z}\left(\nu_z \frac{\partial \bar{u}}{\partial z}\right)$$

$$\frac{\partial \bar{v}}{\partial t} + \bar{u}\frac{\partial \bar{v}}{\partial x} + \bar{v}\frac{\partial \bar{v}}{\partial y} + \bar{w}\frac{\partial \bar{v}}{\partial z} = -\frac{1}{\rho}\frac{\partial \bar{p}}{\partial y} - f\bar{u} + \frac{\partial}{\partial x}\left(\nu_h \frac{\partial \bar{v}}{\partial x}\right)' + \frac{\partial}{\partial y}\left(\nu_h \frac{\partial \bar{v}}{\partial y}\right)$$

$$+ \frac{\partial}{\partial z}\left(\nu_z \frac{\partial \bar{v}}{\partial z}\right)$$

$$-\frac{1}{\rho}\frac{\partial \bar{p}}{\partial z} - g = 0$$

$$\frac{\partial \bar{u}}{\partial x} + \frac{\partial \bar{v}}{\partial y} + \frac{\partial \bar{w}}{\partial z} = 0.$$

Boundary conditions are necessary to solve these equations. These are determined by the nature of the mathematical operators to be solved. Open boundary conditions are dealt with in Section 4.1.3, but those which are necessary are

at the bed $\qquad \bar{u} = 0, \quad \bar{v} = 0, \quad \bar{w} = 0;$

at the surface $\qquad \dfrac{\partial \bar{u}}{\partial z} = 0, \quad \dfrac{\partial \bar{v}}{\partial z} = 0 \quad$ (in the absence of wind).

The pressure, $p$, is equal to the atmospheric pressure (reference pressure) at the surface. At the lateral and the open boundaries, the horizontal components of the flow are taken as $u(z, t)$ and $v(z, t)$.

## 4.1.2 Area of integration

The basic difficulty presented by this model lies in the fact that an area of integration, which is variable in time, has to be taken into account. The essential idea used to solve this type of problem consists of using the curved grid elements which are deformed and which follow the free surface at any given instant. In this case, the variables are simply changed as follows:

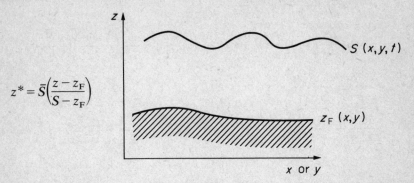

$$z^* = \bar{S}\left(\frac{z - z_F}{S - z_F}\right)$$

where $z_F(x, y)$ represents the elevation of the bed, $S(x, y, t)$ represents the elevation of the surface, $\bar{S}$ is a horizontal reference elevation which is given, for example, by the initial value of the surface. The new system of coordinates, $(x, y, z^*)$, makes it possible to have a fixed integration area. It is still necessary to determine the equations to be solved in the new system.

For any value, the theorem on the derivation of composite functions implies the following relationships:

$$\frac{\partial z^*}{\partial z} = \frac{\bar{S}}{S - z_F}$$

$$\frac{\partial f}{\partial z} = \frac{\partial F}{\partial z^*} \times \frac{\partial z^*}{\partial z} \qquad f(x, y, z, t) = F(x, y, z^*, t)$$

$$\frac{\partial f}{\partial t} = \frac{\partial F}{\partial t} + \frac{\partial F}{\partial z^*} \frac{\partial z^*}{\partial t}$$

$$\frac{\partial f}{\partial x} = \frac{\partial F}{\partial x} + \frac{\partial F}{\partial z^*} \frac{\partial z^*}{\partial x}$$

$$\frac{\partial f}{\partial y} = \frac{\partial F}{\partial y} + \frac{\partial F}{\partial z^*} \frac{\partial z^*}{\partial y} .$$

Let

$$w^* = \frac{\partial z^*}{\partial t} + u\frac{\partial z^*}{\partial x} + v\frac{\partial z^*}{\partial y} + w\frac{\partial z^*}{\partial z},$$

then the momentum equations are obtained:

$$\frac{\partial u}{\partial t} + u\frac{\partial u}{\partial x} + v\frac{\partial u}{\partial y} + w^*\frac{\partial u}{\partial z^*}$$

$$= -g\frac{\partial S}{\partial x} + fv + \frac{\partial}{\partial x}\left(\nu_h\frac{\partial u}{\partial x}\right) + \frac{\partial}{\partial y}\left(\nu_h\frac{\partial u}{\partial y}\right) + \left(\frac{\bar{S}}{S - z_F}\right)^2 \frac{\partial}{\partial z^*}\left(\nu_z\frac{\partial u}{\partial z^*}\right) \quad (4.1)$$

$$\frac{\partial v}{\partial t} + u\frac{\partial v}{\partial x} + v\frac{\partial v}{\partial y} + w^*\frac{\partial v}{\partial z^*}$$

$$= -g\frac{\partial S}{\partial y} - fu + \frac{\partial}{\partial x}\left(\nu_h\frac{\partial v}{\partial x}\right) + \frac{\partial}{\partial y}\left(\nu_h\frac{\partial v}{\partial y}\right) + \frac{\partial}{\partial z^*}\left(\nu_z\frac{\partial v}{\partial z^*}\right)\left(\frac{\bar S}{S - z_F}\right)^2 \quad (4.2)$$

$$-\frac{1}{\rho}\frac{\partial p}{\partial z^*}\frac{\bar S}{S - z_F} - g = 0 \quad (4.3)$$

$$\frac{\partial u}{\partial x} + \frac{\partial v}{\partial y} + \frac{\partial w^*}{\partial z^*} + \frac{1}{S - z_F}\left(\frac{\partial S}{\partial t} + u\frac{\partial S}{\partial x} + v\frac{\partial S}{\partial y}\right) - \frac{1}{S - z_F}\left(u\frac{\partial z_F}{\partial x} + v\frac{\partial z_F}{\partial y}\right) = 0.$$

$$(4.4)$$

These equations represent the evolution in the average values. In order to simplify the actual notation, the bars above these values have been omitted. On the other hand, some terms resulting from horizontal transfer by diffusion were omitted in the variable change in order to simplify the equations in the curved reference system. The horizontal velocity gradients are generally low and the diffusive transfer negligible compared with transfer by convection. Only the vertical transfer by diffusion is of any considerable importance for the solution of the problem.

### 4.1.3  Boundary conditions

As has already been mentioned, boundary conditions are necessary to solve these equations, in particular the vertical profiles of the horizontal components of the velocity. Usually, these values are only incompletely known, and one can only assume that only the mass current can be found, either by measurement or by means of a two-dimensional model for a larger area. Once the mass current is known, it is assumed that the velocity along the edge of the area is that furnished by the Ekman relationship. This means that the integration area will be taken so that it can be assumed that the influence of the relief is sufficiently insignificant along the edge, so as not to create any horizontal velocity gradient. This makes it possible to use the Ekman model. It is assumed that the terms which show the horizontal velocity gradients and the vertical component of the velocity are negligible.

The relationships are the following:

$$\frac{\partial u}{\partial t} = \frac{\partial}{\partial z}\left(\nu_z\frac{\partial u}{\partial z}\right) + fv - \frac{1}{\rho}\frac{\partial p}{\partial x} \quad (4.5)$$

$$\frac{\partial v}{\partial t} = \frac{\partial}{\partial z}\left(\nu_z\frac{\partial v}{\partial z}\right) - fu - \frac{1}{\rho}\frac{\partial p}{\partial y} \quad (4.6)$$

$$\frac{1}{\rho}\frac{\partial p}{\partial z} + g = 0, \quad (4.7)$$

where: at the bed, $u = 0$, $v = 0$; at the surface, $\partial u / \partial z = 0$, $\partial v / \partial z = 0$ in the absence of wind.

If Eq. (4.7) is integrated with respect to $z$ over the range 0 to $H$, the pressure $p$ can be eliminated in Eqs (4.5) and (4.6):

$$-\frac{1}{\rho}\frac{\partial p}{\partial x} = -g\frac{\partial H}{\partial x}$$

$$-\frac{1}{\rho}\frac{\partial p}{\partial y} = -g\frac{\partial H}{\partial y},$$

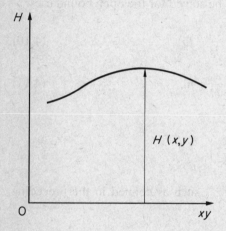

where $H = S - z_{\mathrm{F}}$, and where the atmospheric pressure is taken as the reference pressure. Equations (4.5) and (4.6) then become

$$\frac{\partial u}{\partial t} = \frac{\partial}{\partial z}\left(v_z\frac{\partial u}{\partial z}\right) + fv - g\frac{\partial H}{\partial x} \qquad (4.8)$$

$$\frac{\partial v}{\partial t} = \frac{\partial}{\partial z}\left(v_z\frac{\partial v}{\partial z}\right) - fu - g\frac{\partial H}{\partial y}. \qquad (4.9)$$

The flux is assumed to be known:

$$U = \bar{u} \times H = \int_0^H u \, \mathrm{d}z,$$

with the same applying for $V$. By integrating Eqs (4.8) and (4.9) with respect to $z$, one obtains

$$\frac{\partial}{\partial t}\int_0^H u \, \mathrm{d}z = -\left(v_z\frac{\partial u}{\partial z}\right)_{z=0} + f\int_0^H v \, \mathrm{d}z - gH\frac{\partial H}{\partial x}$$

$$\frac{\partial}{\partial t}\int_0^H v \, \mathrm{d}z = -\left(v_z\frac{\partial v}{\partial z}\right)_{z=0} - f\int_0^H u \, \mathrm{d}z - gH\frac{\partial H}{\partial y},$$

which will make it possible to express the free-surface gradients in terms of known functions, i.e., the flux, $U$ and $V$, or the average velocity, $\bar{u}$ and $\bar{v}$, and its variation as a function of time. Thus

$$-g\frac{\partial H}{\partial x}=\frac{1}{H}\frac{\partial(\bar{u}H)}{\partial t}+\frac{\tau_{x0}}{H}-f\bar{v}$$

$$-g\frac{\partial H}{\partial y}=\frac{1}{H}\frac{\partial(\bar{v}H)}{\partial t}+\frac{\tau_{y0}}{H}+f\bar{u},$$

which yields the two relationships to be solved for the open boundaries:

$$\frac{\partial u}{\partial t}=\frac{\partial}{\partial z}\left(\nu_z\frac{\partial u}{\partial z}\right)+fv+\frac{1}{H}\frac{\partial(\bar{u}H)}{\partial t}+\frac{\tau_{x0}}{H}-f\bar{v} \tag{4.10}$$

$$\frac{\partial v}{\partial t}=\frac{\partial}{\partial z}\left(\nu_z\frac{\partial v}{\partial z}\right)-fu+\frac{1}{H}\frac{\partial(\bar{v}H)}{\partial t}+\frac{\tau_{y0}}{H}+f\bar{u}, \tag{4.11}$$

with

$$\tau_{x0}=\nu_z\frac{\partial u}{\partial z}\bigg|_{z=0} \quad \text{and} \quad \tau_{y0}=\nu_z\frac{\partial v}{\partial z}\bigg|_{z=0}.$$

Considering the variable change in $z^*$, such as defined in the preceding section, namely,

$$z^*=\bar{S}\frac{z-z_F}{S-z_F}$$

with the variables $u$ and $v$ as functions of $x$, $y$, $z^*$ and $t$, Eqs (4.10) and (4.11) become

$$\frac{\partial u}{\partial t}-\frac{z^*}{S-z_F}\frac{\partial H}{\partial t}\frac{\partial u}{\partial z^*}=\left(\frac{\bar{S}}{S-z_F}\right)^2\frac{\partial}{\partial z^*}\left(\nu_z\frac{\partial u}{\partial z^*}\right)+fv+\frac{1}{H}\frac{\partial\bar{u}H}{\partial t}+\frac{\tau_{x0}}{S-z_F}-f\bar{v}$$

$$\frac{\partial v}{\partial t}-\frac{z^*}{S-z_F}\frac{\partial H}{\partial t}\frac{\partial v}{\partial z^*}=\left(\frac{\bar{S}}{S-z_F}\right)^2\frac{\partial}{\partial z^*}\left(\nu_z\frac{\partial v}{\partial z^*}\right)-fu+\frac{1}{H}\frac{\partial\bar{v}H}{\partial t}+\frac{\tau_{y0}}{S-z_F}+f\bar{u}.$$

It is assumed that the free surface changes slowly as a function of time and that it is possible to ignore the terms in $\partial H/\partial t$, which means that the relationships are simplified and are such that the source terms are independent of the elevation, $z$:

$$\frac{\partial u}{\partial t}=\left(\frac{\bar{S}}{S-z_F}\right)^2\frac{\partial}{\partial z^*}\left(\nu_z\frac{\partial u}{\partial z^*}\right)+fv+\frac{\partial u}{\partial t}+\frac{\tau_{x0}}{S-z_F}-f\bar{v} \tag{4.12}$$

$$\frac{\partial v}{\partial t}=\left(\frac{\bar{S}}{S-z_F}\right)^2\frac{\partial}{\partial z^*}\left(\nu_z\frac{\partial u}{\partial z^*}\right)-fu+\frac{\partial\bar{v}}{\partial t}+\frac{\tau_{y0}}{S-z_F}+f\bar{u}. \tag{4.13}$$

In these relationships, which make it possible to determine the vertical profile of the horizontal velocities, $u$ and $v$, at the open boundaries of the area, terms appear which represent the turbulent fluxes of momentum, as is the case of the general equations within the area. It was decided to determine them with the help of the eddy viscosity. This is explained below.

### 4.1.4 Simulation of turbulence: evaluation of eddy viscosity

A distinction is made between horizontal and vertical exchanges. It can be assumed that the horizontal velocity gradients are much weaker than the vertical gradients and that transport by convection predominates over transport by diffusion. In other words, an arbitrary horizontal diffusion coefficient (from a reasonable range of values) can be taken. It was possible to check subsequently that these values have very little influence upon the results. On the other hand, the vertical diffusive exchanges are not negligible compared with convection, because the latter is very weak. It is therefore necessary to pay special attention to them. These exchanges depend upon many parameters such as, for example, the roughness and the topography of the bed, etc. It is therefore necessary that the evaluation of these coefficients for turbulent diffusion as a function of the elevation be accurate in order to obtain a good representation of the bed boundary layer.

A very classical model based upon the idea of a macroscale of turbulence (mixing length) was adopted here:

$$\nu_z = l^2 \sqrt{\left(\frac{\partial u}{\partial z}\right)^2 + \left(\frac{\partial v}{\partial z}\right)^2},$$

where $l = kz$, if $z < \Delta$ and $l = k\Delta$, if $z > \Delta$, where $\Delta = \alpha(S - z_F)$, $k$ being the Kármán constant and $z$ the distance to the bed. The following values were used for a highly turbulent flow; $k \simeq 0.4$ and $\alpha = 0.2$.

In the system of coordinates in $x$, $y$ and $z^*$, this is written:

$$\nu_z = l^2 \sqrt{\left(\frac{\partial u}{\partial z^*}\right)^2 + \left(\frac{\partial v}{\partial z^*}\right)^2} \left(\frac{\bar{S}}{S - z_F}\right),$$

where

$$l = k \frac{S - z_F}{\bar{S}} z^*.$$

The system of equations obtained is now complete, and it is necessary to attempt to solve the system. This is dealt with in the next section.

## 4.2 Algorithm

Due to the large number of unknowns and computation points in the area, a completely implicit solution of the entire body of equations would lead to excessive storage requirements and prohibitive computation time. On the other hand, a completely explicit solution would result in restrictions upon the time-step which will be determined for the various solution stages. Restrictions upon the time-step are

(1) Surface-wave stability along the two horizontal directions:

$$\Delta T \leq \min \left( \frac{\Delta x}{\sqrt{g(S - z_F)}}, \frac{\Delta y}{\sqrt{g(S - z_F)}} \right).$$

(2) Stability for horizontal and vertical diffusion:

$$\Delta T \leq \min \left( \frac{\Delta x^2}{2\nu_h}, \frac{\Delta y^2}{2\nu_h} \right) \quad \text{and} \quad \Delta T \leq \frac{\Delta z^2}{2\nu_z}.$$

(3) Stability for horizontal and vertical convection:

$$\Delta T \leq \min \left( \frac{\Delta x}{u}, \frac{\Delta y}{v}, \frac{\Delta z}{w} \right).$$

For a channel in shallow water, the orders of magnitude of the variables are as follows:

$\Delta x = \Delta y = 100 \text{ m}$

$\nu_h$ variable from 1 to $10^{-3} \text{ m}^2/\text{s}$

$u = 0.5$ to 1 m/s.

$\nu_z = 5 \times 10^{-2} \text{ m}^2/\text{s}$

$\Delta z = 0.15$ to 2 m

$S - z_F = \text{depth} = 20 \text{ m}$

which yield

$$\underbrace{\frac{\Delta x}{\sqrt{g(S - z_F)}}, \frac{\Delta y}{\sqrt{g(S - z_F)}}}_{7 \text{ s}} \quad \underbrace{\frac{\Delta x^2}{2\nu_h}, \frac{\Delta y^2}{2\nu_h}}_{100 \text{ s}}, \underbrace{\frac{\Delta z^2}{2\nu_z}}_{10 \text{ s}} \quad \underbrace{\frac{\Delta x}{u}, \frac{\Delta y}{v}, \frac{\Delta z}{v}}_{100 \text{ s}}$$

Among all these restrictions upon the time-step, the most inconvenient are those which affect the determination of the free-surface waves and the vertical diffusion. These restrictions result from the use of the so-called fractionary step method for the solution of these equations. This method is based upon the implicit or explicit solution of successive stages.

It is assumed that the variables at time $n \, \mathrm{d}t$ are known. The values at time $(n+1)\,dt$ are found by going through intermediate values determined as follows in Sections 4.2.1 to 4.2.3, where the indices $1, 2, \ldots, n, n+1$ are the indices which correspond to the various steps.

## 4.2.1 Horizontal convection diffusion

*Step 1* Horizontal convection diffusion. This is handled explicitly:

$$
\frac{u^{(1)} - u^{(n)}}{dt} + u^{(n)} \frac{\partial u^{(n)}}{\partial x} + v^{(n)} \frac{\partial u^{(n)}}{\partial y} + w^{*(n)} \frac{\partial u^{(n)}}{\partial z^*}
$$
$$
= \frac{\partial}{\partial x} \left( \nu_\mathrm{h} \frac{\partial u^{(n)}}{\partial x} \right) + \frac{\partial}{\partial y} \left( \nu_\mathrm{h} \frac{\partial u^{(n)}}{\partial y} \right) \quad (4.14)
$$

$$
\frac{v^{(1)} - v^{(n)}}{dt} + u^{(n)} \frac{\partial v^{(n)}}{\partial x} + v^{(n)} \frac{\partial v^{(n)}}{\partial y} + w^{*(n)} \frac{\partial v^{(n)}}{\partial z^*}
$$
$$
= \frac{\partial}{\partial y} \left( \nu_\mathrm{h} \frac{\partial v^{(n)}}{\partial x} \right) + \frac{\partial}{\partial y} \left( \nu_\mathrm{h} \frac{\partial v^{(n)}}{\partial y} \right). \quad (4.15)
$$

The same grid size is used for the three components of the velocity. The convection terms are discretized by introducing up winding and then interpolating parabolically. The method is very close to that described by Daubert (1974). As far as the diffusion terms are concerned, they are discretized in a traditional manner and centred. The discretization is completely explicit, and the time-step must obey the restrictions for the operators so that the computations do not become unstable.

## 4.2.2 Vertical diffusion

*Step 2* Vertical diffusion:

$$
\frac{u^{(2)} - u^{(1)}}{dt} = \frac{\partial}{\partial z^*} \left( \nu_z^{(n)} \frac{\partial u^{(2)}}{\partial z^*} \right) \left( \frac{\bar{S}}{S - z_\mathrm{F}} \right)^2 + f v^{(2)} \quad (4.16)
$$

$$
\frac{v^{(2)} - v^{(1)}}{dt} = \frac{\partial}{\partial z^*} \left( \nu_z^{(n)} \frac{\partial v^{(2)}}{\partial z^*} \right) \left( \frac{\bar{S}}{S - z_\mathrm{F}} \right)^2 - f u^{(2)}. \quad (4.17)
$$

This step, which only involves a single direction in space, is discretized in a traditional manner and is not centred. The system obtained is solved by double sweeping, and both $u^{(2)}$ and $v^{(2)}$ are taken simultaneously as unknowns (see Section 2.1.3).

It should be noted that the discretization employed is completely implicit, and the numerical scheme is therefore unconditionally stable.

## 4.2.3 Continuity equation

*Step 3* Computation of the free surface and the vertical velocity by means of the continuity equation.

This step is the most delicate, and the corresponding equations are

$$\frac{u^{(n+1)} - u^{(2)}}{dt} = -\frac{1}{\rho}\frac{\partial p^{(n+1)}}{\partial x} - g\frac{z^*}{\bar{S}}\frac{\partial S^{(n+1)}}{\partial x} - g\frac{\bar{S} - z^*}{\bar{S}}\frac{\partial z_F}{\partial x} \tag{4.18}$$

$$\frac{v^{(n+1)} - v^{(2)}}{dt} = -\frac{1}{\rho}\frac{\partial p^{(n+1)}}{\partial y} - g\frac{z^*}{\bar{S}}\frac{\partial S^{(n+1)}}{\partial y} - g\frac{\bar{S} - z^*}{\bar{S}}\frac{\partial z_F}{\partial y} \tag{4.19}$$

$$\frac{1}{\rho}\frac{\partial p^{(n+1)}}{\partial z^*} = -g\frac{S^{(n+1)} - z_F}{\bar{S}} \tag{4.20}$$

$$\frac{\partial u^{(n+1)}}{\partial x} + \frac{\partial v^{(n+1)}}{\partial y} + \frac{\partial w^{*(n+1)}}{\partial z^*} + \frac{1}{S - z_F}\left(\frac{\partial S}{\partial t} + u\frac{\partial S}{\partial x} + v\frac{\partial S}{\partial y}\right)$$

$$-\frac{1}{S - z_F}\left(u\frac{\partial z_F}{\partial x} + v\frac{\partial z_F}{\partial y}\right) = 0. \tag{4.21}$$

Equation (4.20) is integrated immediately to yield

$$p = P_0 - \rho g\frac{S - z_F}{\bar{S}}(z^* - \bar{S}),$$

where $P_0$ represents the atmospheric pressure and is assumed constant. This equation makes it possible to eliminate the pressure, and Eqs (4.18) and (4.19) become

$$\frac{u^{(n+1)} - u^{(2)}}{dt} = -g\frac{\partial S^{(n+1)}}{\partial x} \tag{4.22}$$

$$\frac{v^{(n+1)} - v^{(2)}}{dt} = -g\frac{\partial S^{(n+1)}}{\partial y}. \tag{4.23}$$

This elimination highly simplifies the solution. If the density of the fluid is no longer constant, it is no longer possible to obtain such a simple formula, but the procedure essentially remains the same.

If $u_m$ and $v_m$ represent the horizontal components of the average vertical velocity, then

$$u_m = \frac{1}{\bar{S}}\int_0^{\bar{S}} u \, dz^*$$

$$v_m = \frac{1}{\bar{S}}\int_0^{\bar{S}} v \, dz^*.$$

The vertical integration of Eqs (4.21), (4.22) and (4.23) on the basis of the impermeability conditions at the bed and at the surface (i.e., $w^*(0) =$

$w^*(\bar{S}) = 0)$ yields

$$\frac{\bar{S}\tilde{u}_m - \bar{S}u_m^{(2)}}{dt} = -g\bar{S}\frac{\partial S}{\partial x} \qquad (4.24)$$

$$\frac{\bar{S}\tilde{v}_m - \bar{S}v_m^{(2)}}{dt} = -g\bar{S}\frac{\partial S}{\partial y} \qquad (4.25)$$

and

$$\frac{\partial S}{\partial t} + \frac{\partial \tilde{u}_m(S - z_F)}{\partial x} + \frac{\partial \tilde{v}_m(S - z_F)}{\partial y} = 0. \qquad (4.26)$$

By multiplying Eqs (4.24) and (4.25) by $(S - z_F)$, one obtains the classical equations for long linear waves with boundary conditions for the current (see Section 2.1). The solution is analogous to that described in Section 2.3. In the course of the tests carried out, it became evident that it is better to discretize Eqs (4.21), (4.22) and (4.23) and integrate them to obtain the *compatible* discretization of Eqs (4.24), (4.25) and (4.26).

If $S^{(n+1)}$ is known, it is only necessary to use Eqs (4.22) and (4.23) to obtain $u^{(n+1)}$ and $v^{(n+1)}$. By means of the continuity equation integrated either on the basis of the free surface or on the basis of the bed, $w^{*(n+1)}$ is obtained without any difficulty.

## 4.3 Validity of model

It was decided to test the model by means of a laboratory experiment. A channel, inclined at 45° to the direction of the mean current, was created in a straight flume. The main dimensions are given in Fig. 4.1. Different

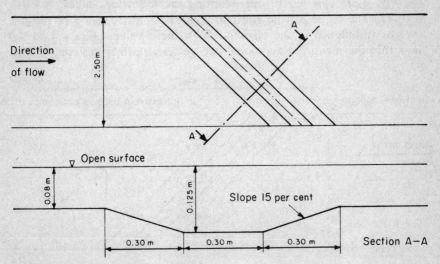

*Fig. 4.1* Schematic view of channel

*Fig. 4.2* View from above flow: exposure 15 s

profiles were obtained for the horizontal velocity measurements by means of a propeller, and they showed considerable deviation in the vicinity of the bed of the channel. The surface flow was visualized by means of floats (white lines), and the flow at the bed was illustrated by means of grains of permanganate dye (Fig. 4.2).

It was possible to determine that the upstream velocity conditions were quite stable, and the coefficients of the turbulence model were taken so as to obtain a velocity profile as close as possible to that measured at point 2 (see Fig. 4.3). This led to our adopting the following values: $\alpha = 0.2$, $k = 0.12$. The value for the Kármán constant is low because of the low level of turbulence in the channel. With these values, Figs 4.4 to 4.9 show that the measured and computed velocity profiles are comparable.

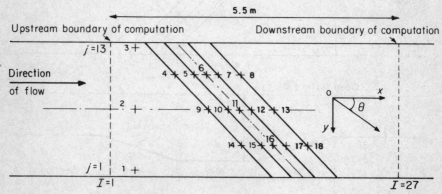

*Fig. 4.3* Location of measurement points

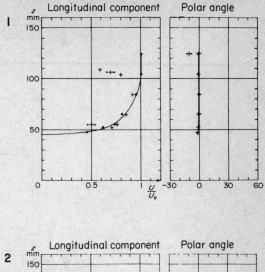

● Computation

+ Measured values

✛ Range of uncertainty

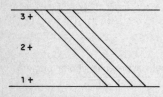

Point 1, $z_F$ = 0.045 m

Point 2, $z_F$ = 0.045 m

Point 3, $z_F$ = 0.045 m

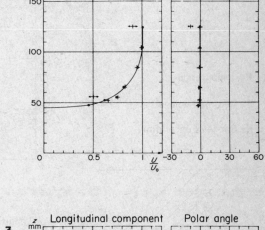

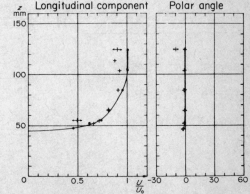

*Fig. 4.4* Vertical velocity profiles: comparison of computations and experimental results for points 1, 2 and 3. Test conditions: Reynolds number, $R_0 = 2.5 \times 10^4$; Froude number, $F_r^2 = 5 \times 10^{-2}$; water depth, $H = 0.125$ m; mean velocity in the flume, $V_0 = 0.17$ m/s

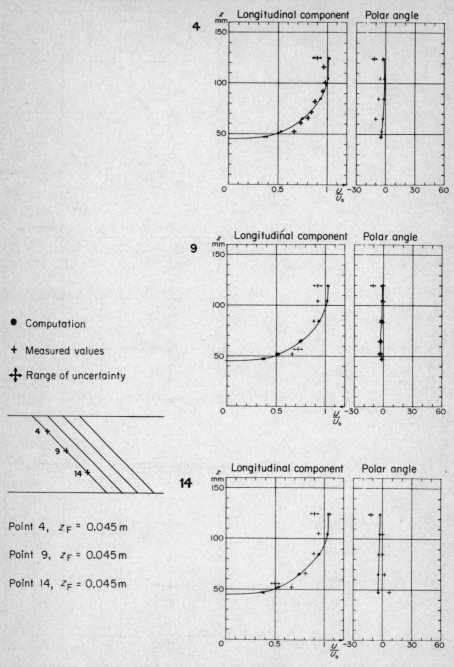

*Fig. 4.5* Vertical velocity profiles: comparison of computations and experimental results for points 4, 9 and 14. Test conditions: $R_0 = 2.5 \times 10^4$; $F_r^2 = 5 \times 10^{-2}$; $H = 0.125$ m; $V_0 = 0.17$ m/s

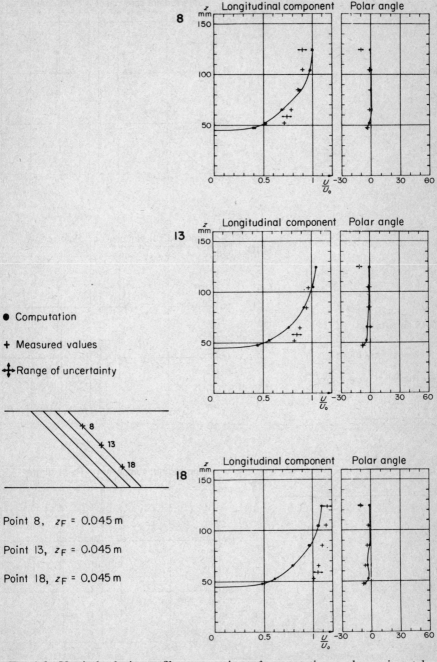

- ● Computation
- + Measured values
- ✛ Range of uncertainty

Point 8, $z_F$ = 0.045 m

Point 13, $z_F$ = 0.045 m

Point 18, $z_F$ = 0.045 m

**Fig. 4.6** Vertical velocity profiles: comparison of computations and experimental results for points 8, 13 and 18. Test conditions: $R_0 = 2.5 \times 10^4$; $F_r^2 = 5 \times 10^{-2}$; $H = 0.125$ m; $V_0 = 0.17$ m/s

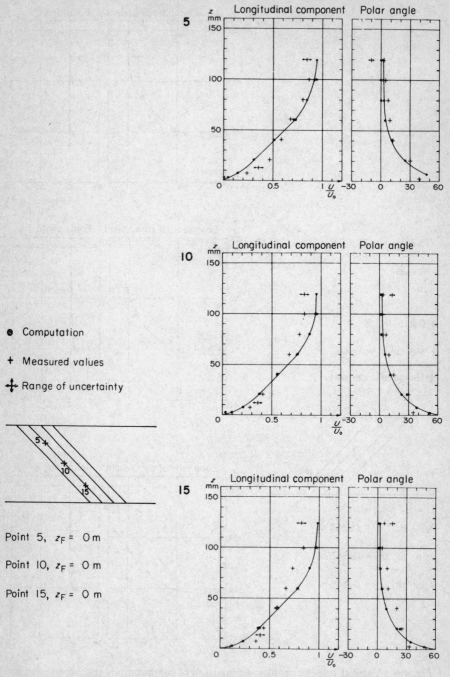

*Fig. 4.7* Vertical velocity profiles: comparison of computations and experimental results for points 5, 10 and 15. Test conditions: $R_0 = 2.5 \times 10^4$; $F_r^2 = 5 \times 10^{-2}$; $H = 0.125$ m; $V_0 = 0.17$ m/s

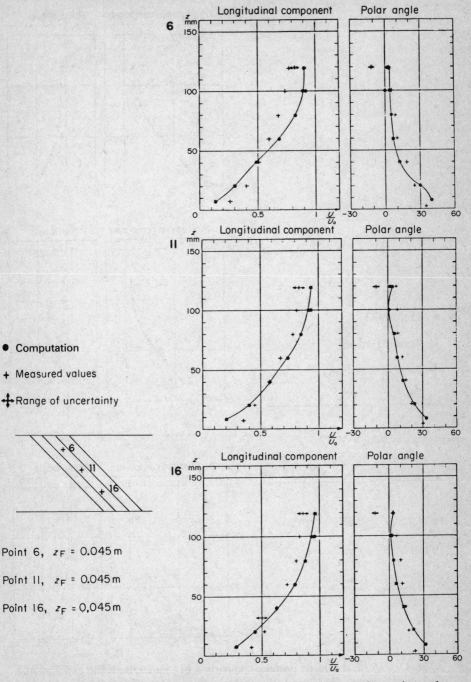

*Fig. 4.8* Vertical velocity profiles: comparison of computations and experimental results for points 6, 11 and 16. Test conditions: $R_0 = 2.5 \times 10^4$; $F_r^2 = 5 \times 10^{-2}$; $H = 0.125$ m; $V_0 = 0.17$ m/s

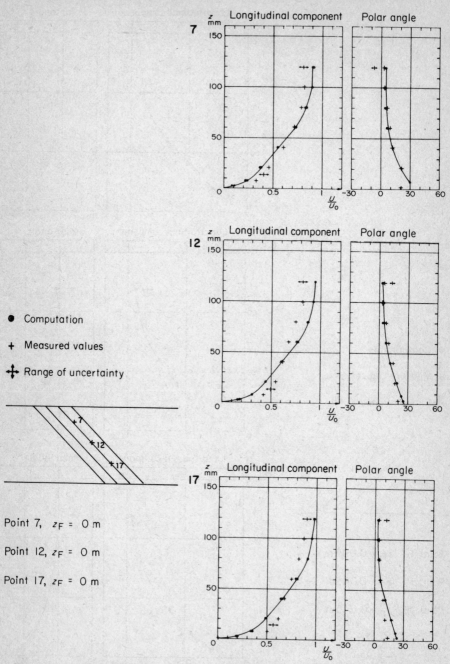

Fig. 4.9 Vertical velocity profiles: comparison of computations and experimental results for points 7, 12 and 17. Test conditions: $R_0 = 2.5 \times 10^4$; $F_r^2 = 5 \times 10^{-2}$; $H = 0.125$ m; $V_0 = 0.17$ m/s

The computations reproduce the important deviation of the current quite faithfully, and the deviation is restricted to a zone near the bed by the effects of advection.

A significant difference is seen between the measurements and the computed values in the vicinity of the vertical walls of the flume (point 1, for example). This is due to the effects of the boundary layers which develop in these zones and which are not represented in the computations.

*Note:* A two-dimensional version of this model can be obtained by integrating the equations in one of the horizontal directions. This would be for application in the case of estuaries. The equations of the model and their solution are of the same type as above. The equations are 'closed' by using additional assumptions, mainly for the spatial integration of the non-linear convection terms. The model has been completely described by Davesne (1978). It was applied to the study of the movement of silt in the Gironde estuary.

In conclusion, it would seem that by setting the level of turbulence, which requires a knowledge of at least a velocity profile in the area being investigated, the computation code makes it possible to determine, with good precision, the effect of deviations due to the topography of the bed. This model is at the point of being coupled with a model for determining the current of local tides, and the latter would provide the boundary conditions for the mass current to be assigned. This should make it possible to eliminate some of the difficulties encountered in the investigation of the movement of sediment or, more generally, when the flow has a highly three-dimensional structure, as is the case in the following chapter, which deals with wind-generated currents.

# Part 2 Lakes and rivers

# 5 Wind-generated currents

## 5.1 Introduction

Generally, predicting the characteristics of currents in lakes is a complex task since, in most cases, these currents are influenced mainly by the wind and the density gradients resulting from exchanges between the water and the atmosphere. The methods which can be used for that purpose are also applicable to tideless seas, such as the Mediterranean. However, it should be noted that, in this field, the use of models is still at an early stage, which explains why we shall not dwell on this aspect.

## 5.2 Models of wind-generated currents

Modelling wind-generated currents is a rather complex problem, since the wind produces a substantial heterogeneity in the vertical component of velocity. Therefore, generally, a two-dimensional approach proves inadequate. In fact, wherever a solid boundary exists, the action of the wind at the surface always induces return currents at the bed. Moreover, the mixing process is less pronounced in the vertical direction and noticeable density gradients can be observed.

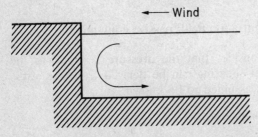

At the outset, the equations describing the motion are those of Navier–Stokes, into which an external force representing the Coriolis acceleration has been introduced. These equations must be solved in a variable field, since the flow may be influenced by the free surface. Such is the case when the tide and the wind have a combined action. The wind exerts a given shearing stress at the surface. However, even if the free surface is assumed to be fixed, these three-dimensional equations cannot be solved on a large scale. An examination of the velocity field generated by the wind shows that, in most cases, the acceleration in the vertical direction is small and negligible compared with gravity. In addition, assuming that only the vertical turbulent transfers are meaningful, the equations of the model can be written as follows:

$$
\left.
\begin{aligned}
& \frac{\partial \bar{u}}{\partial x} + \frac{\partial \bar{v}}{\partial y} + \frac{\partial \bar{w}}{\partial z} = 0 \\[2mm]
& \frac{\partial \bar{u}}{\partial t} + \bar{u}\frac{\partial \bar{u}}{\partial x} + \bar{v}\frac{\partial \bar{u}}{\partial y} + \bar{w}\frac{\partial \bar{u}}{\partial z} = \frac{\partial}{\partial z}\left(\nu_z \frac{\partial \bar{u}}{\partial z}\right) - \frac{1}{\rho_0}\frac{\partial \bar{P}'}{\partial x} + 2\boldsymbol{\Omega} \times \mathbf{V}\,|_x \\[2mm]
& \frac{\partial \bar{v}}{\partial t} + u\frac{\partial \bar{v}}{\partial x} + v\frac{\partial \bar{v}}{\partial y} + w\frac{\partial \bar{v}}{\partial y} = \frac{\partial}{\partial z}\left(\nu_z \frac{\partial \bar{v}}{\partial z}\right) - \frac{1}{\rho_0}\frac{\partial \bar{P}'}{\partial y} + 2\boldsymbol{\Omega} \times \mathbf{V}\,|_y \\[2mm]
& 0 = -\frac{1}{\rho_0}\frac{\partial \bar{P}'}{\partial z} - \frac{\rho - \rho_0}{\rho_0}\,g \\[2mm]
& \frac{\partial \bar{\theta}}{\partial t} + \bar{u}\frac{\partial \bar{\theta}}{\partial x} + \bar{v}\frac{\partial \bar{\theta}}{\partial y} + \bar{w}\frac{\partial \bar{\theta}}{\partial z} = \frac{\partial}{\partial z}\left(\nu_{\theta z}\frac{\partial \bar{\theta}}{\partial z}\right) \\[2mm]
& \frac{\partial \bar{c}}{\partial t} + \bar{u}\frac{\partial \bar{c}}{\partial x} + \bar{v}\frac{\partial \bar{c}}{\partial y} + \bar{w}\frac{\partial \bar{c}}{\partial z} = \frac{\partial}{\partial z}\left(\nu_{\theta z}\frac{\partial \bar{c}}{\partial z}\right)
\end{aligned}
\right\} \quad (5.1)
$$

where

$\bar{u},\ \bar{v},\ \bar{w}$    are the three components of velocity

$\boldsymbol{\Omega}$    is the Earth's rotation vector. The effects of the induced acceleration is neglected. Only the Coriolis acceleration is taken into account

$\bar{P}'$    is the difference between the pressure field, $\bar{P}$, and the hydrostatic field

$\bar{\theta}$    is the thermal field

$\bar{c}$    represents any concentration field: passive contaminant

At the free surface, we consider that the pressure is equal to the atmospheric pressure and that shearing can be derived from the stress exerted by the wind, which is assumed to be known:

$$
\tau_{x(\text{wind})} = \rho_0\left(\nu_z \frac{\partial u}{\partial z}\right)
$$

$$
\tau_{y(\text{wind})} = \rho_0\left(\nu_z \frac{\partial v}{\partial z}\right).
$$

For that purpose, we shall use a formula which establishes a relation between shearing stress, $\tau$, and wind velocity, $W$, as follows:

$$\tau = C_d \rho_a \|W\| W,$$

where $\rho_a$ is the density of air, $C_d \simeq 0.9 \times 10^{-3}$ when $W < 10 \, \text{m/s}$, and $C_d \simeq 2.9 \times 10^{-3}$ when $W > 10 \, \text{m/s}$. The sudden variation of the friction coefficient in relation to the wind velocity can be explained by the fact that the behaviour of the open surface changes when the wind velocity exceeds $10 \, \text{m/s}$.

The pressure can be obtained by integration along the vertical axis. Assuming free-surface conditions, the formula is as follows:

$$P'(x, y, z, t) = \int_Z^z \rho'(u) g \, du + \rho_0 g Z + P_{atm}(x, y).$$

This model is very close to that previously described. In this case, the thermal field and the concentration field, $c$, have an impact on the velocity field as a result of buoyancy. The solution of these equations is re-examined in Part 3, in our study of atmospheric phenomena.

At the outset, this model can be considered as adequate in the case of wind-generated flows into stratified ambient fluids. In addition, if the space–velocity gradient is not too high (i.e., if the topography of the bed is fairly homogeneous), another simplification can be made. In numerous cases, the velocities generated by the wind are small. The velocity at the surface can be considered as about 2 per cent of that of the wind. Assuming that space–velocity gradients are small, i.e., considering the case for low-velocity flows, the quadratic acceleration terms can be neglected. The dynamic equations can then be expressed as follows:

$$\left.\begin{aligned}
&\frac{\partial \bar{u}}{\partial x} + \frac{\partial \bar{v}}{\partial y} + \frac{\partial \bar{w}}{\partial z} = 0 \\[2mm]
&\frac{\partial \bar{u}}{\partial t} = \frac{\partial}{\partial z}\left(\nu_z \frac{\partial \bar{u}}{\partial z}\right) - g\frac{\partial Z}{\partial x} - \frac{1}{\rho_0}\frac{\partial P_{atm}}{\partial x} + \frac{\rho'(Z)}{\rho_0} g\frac{\partial Z}{\partial x} \\[2mm]
&\qquad\qquad\qquad\qquad - \frac{1}{\rho_0}\int_Z^z \frac{\partial \rho'}{\partial x} g \, du + 2\boldsymbol{\Omega} \times \mathbf{V}\big|_x \\[2mm]
&\frac{\partial \bar{v}}{\partial t} = \frac{\partial}{\partial z}\left(\nu_z \frac{\partial \bar{v}}{\partial z}\right) - g\frac{\partial Z}{\partial y} - \frac{1}{\rho_0}\frac{\partial P_{atm}}{\partial y} + \frac{\rho'(Z)}{\rho_0} g\frac{\partial Z}{\partial y} \\[2mm]
&\qquad\qquad\qquad\qquad - \frac{1}{\rho_0}\int_Z^z \frac{\partial \rho'}{\partial y} g \, du + 2\boldsymbol{\Omega} \times \mathbf{V}\big|_y
\end{aligned}\right\} \quad (5.2)$$

If the fluid is isothermal and the pollutant does not result in density variations, then $\rho' = 0$. Through a vertical integration of these equations, the following dynamic equations can be obtained:

$$
\left.
\begin{array}{l}
\dfrac{\partial Z}{\partial t}+\dfrac{\partial(\bar{u}h)}{\partial x}+\dfrac{\partial(\bar{v}h)}{\partial y}=0 \\[2mm]
\dfrac{\partial(\bar{u}h)}{\partial t}=-gh\dfrac{\partial Z}{\partial x}+f\bar{u}h-\dfrac{1}{\rho_0}h\dfrac{\partial P_{atm}}{\partial x}+\dfrac{1}{\rho_0}\tau_{x(wind)}+\dfrac{1}{\rho_0}\tau_{x(bed)}+f\bar{u}h \\[2mm]
\dfrac{\partial(\bar{v}h)}{\partial t}=-gh\dfrac{\partial Z}{\partial y}-f\bar{u}h-\dfrac{1}{\rho_0}h\dfrac{\partial P_{atm}}{\partial y}+\dfrac{1}{\rho_0}\tau_{y(wind)}+\dfrac{1}{\rho_0}\tau_{y(bed)}-f\bar{u}h
\end{array}
\right\}
\quad (5.3)
$$

where

$\bar{u}, \bar{v}$  are the horizontal components of the average velocity

$h$  is the depth

$Z$  is the elevation of the free surface

$\left.\begin{array}{l}\tau_{x(wind)}\\ \tau_{y(wind)}\end{array}\right\}$ are the components of the stress exerted by the wind

$\left.\begin{array}{l}\tau_{x(bed)}\\ \tau_{y(bed)}\end{array}\right\}$ are the components of the stress exerted by the bed

$f$ is the Coriolis parameter which depends on latitude.

At this stage, it appears that, by introducing a phenomenological law which establishes a relation between the stress exerted by the bed and the average motion, it is possible to determine the average flow, then to derive from this value the slope of the free surface and, finally, to solve the local dynamic equation which provides the velocity field on the vertical. This method brings in a marked simplification in the solution of the equation.

In order to solve Eqs (5.2) and to determine the velocity at any point in the computing field, it is necessary first to solve Eqs (5.3), using a method absolutely identical to that described in Section 2.3. Once the gradient of the free surface is known, the solution of the two equations of system (5.2) can be obtained as follows:

$$
\left.
\begin{array}{l}
\dfrac{\partial \bar{u}}{\partial t}-\dfrac{\partial}{\partial z}\left(\nu_z\dfrac{\partial \bar{u}}{\partial z}\right)=F_1 \\[3mm]
\dfrac{\partial \bar{v}}{\partial t}-\dfrac{\partial}{\partial z}\left(\nu_z\dfrac{\partial \bar{v}}{\partial z}\right)=F_2
\end{array}
\right\}
\quad (5.4)
$$

With the following boundary conditions:

$$
\tau_{vx}=C_d\rho_a W_x\|W\|=\rho_0\nu_z\dfrac{\partial \bar{u}}{\partial z}
$$

(at the surface)

$$
\tau_{vy}=C_d\rho_a W_y\|W\|=\rho_0\nu_z\dfrac{\partial \bar{v}}{\partial z}
$$

and

$$\tau_{fx} = \frac{g}{C^2} \rho_0 \bar{u} \sqrt{\bar{u}^2 + \bar{v}^2} = \rho_0 \nu_z \frac{\partial \bar{u}}{\partial z}$$
$$\tau_{fy} = \frac{g}{C^2} \rho_0 \bar{v} \sqrt{\bar{u}^2 + \bar{v}^2} = \rho_0 \nu_z \frac{\partial \bar{v}}{\partial z}$$

(at the bed),

$F_1$ and $F_2$, $\bar{u}$ and $\bar{v}$ are determined by solving Eqs (5.3). The solution of Eqs (5.4), following discretization, is obtained in a classical way by double sweeping. The vertical component, $w$, of the velocity can be determined by integrating the continuity equation, starting from the bed, where it is known:

$$w(z) - w_{(bed)} = - \int_{z(bed)}^{z} \left( \frac{\partial \bar{u}}{\partial x} + \frac{\partial \bar{v}}{\partial y} \right) dz$$

with

$$w_{(bed)} = \bar{u}_{(bed)} \frac{\partial z_F}{\partial x} + \bar{v} \frac{\partial z_F}{\partial y}$$

and $z_F$ = bed elevation.

This type of model has been applied to the Mediterranean Sea. Figures 5.1($a$) to 5.1($d$) describe the surface current induced by a NE wind with a velocity of 16 m/s in the Bay of Cannes. It can be noted that current parallel to the coast-line appears for a short distance. In the open sea, the deviation of the current with respect to the veering of the wind is 45° (classical Ekman model). At a depth of 60 m, the deviation of the currents changes. This is due both to the topography of the bed and to the presence of solid boundaries. The order of magnitude of the velocities is fully consistent with the measured values. Based on this velocity field, it is possible to get the bacterial pollution generated by a sea-outfall in the bay.

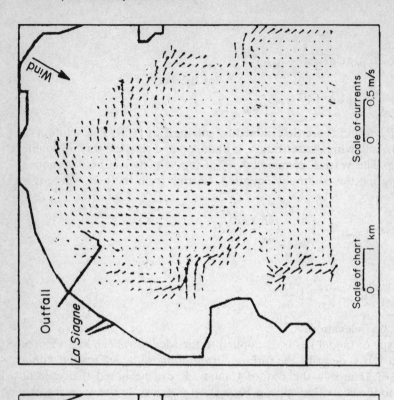

*Fig. 5.1(b)* Wind-induced currents in the Bay of Cannes. Wind velocity: 16 m/s. Currents to a depth of −60 m

*Fig. 5.1(a)* Wind-induced currents in the Bay of Cannes. Wind velocity: 16 m/s. Surface currents

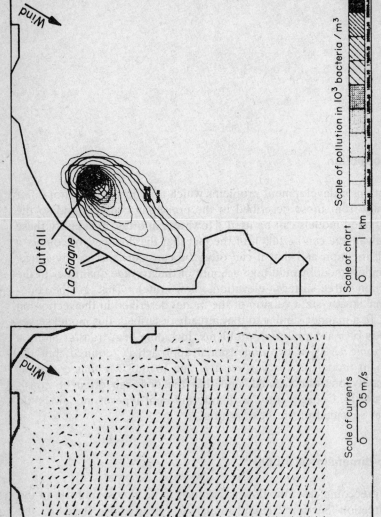

*Fig. 5.1(c)* Wind-induced currents in the Bay of Cannes. Wind velocity: 16 m/s. Currents to a depth of −5 m

*Fig. 5.1(d)* Wind-induced currents in the Bay of Cannes. Wind velocity: 16 m/s. Pollution from outfall bacteria

# 6 Flow in rivers

## 6.1 Introduction

The pollution or development problems which arise in rivers do not differ substantially from those described in the preceding chapters and so the aforementioned models can be used. However, in order to simplify these models, advantage can be taken of the fact that the flow has, of course, a privileged direction and that it can often be considered as steady-state.

The simplest model would take account of the average quantities in the river section (free-surface elevation, flow rate). This is the one-dimensional steady-state version of the model described in the section on tidal seas. In a manner similar to that already described, this model serves in the study of many pollution problems, including heat transfer along a river. In some cases, a two-dimensional approach is required, but the Saint-Venant model proves very costly, due to the fact that a river is predominantly one-dimensional, and that the flow can often be considered as steady. Consequently, a slightly different type of model should be used, as specified in the next section.

## 6.2 Two-dimensional model

As in the preceding case, the flow is assumed to be almost uniform in the vertical direction (Section 2.1) and similar to a steady flow. Based on the overall profile of a river, a grid which takes the exact shape of the river is defined in order to obtain a satisfactory description of the geometry without having to perform calculations on too many points.

### 6.2.1 Equations of the problem

The basic assumptions are those already made for the study of long waves, with two additional considerations:

(1) the flow is steady;

(2) the slope of the free surface varies little in space and it is admitted that the approximate height of water is known (through a one-dimensional model).

Based on these assumptions, the equations of the problem are as follows:

$$\frac{\partial(uh)}{\partial x} + \frac{\partial(vh)}{\partial y} = 0 \tag{6.1}$$

$$u\frac{\partial u}{\partial x} + v\frac{\partial u}{\partial y} = \frac{1}{h}\frac{\partial}{\partial x}\left(vh\frac{\partial u}{\partial x}\right) + \frac{1}{h}\frac{\partial}{\partial y}\left(vh\frac{\partial u}{\partial y}\right) - g\frac{\partial Z}{\partial x} - \frac{g}{Kh^{\frac{4}{3}}}u\sqrt{u^2+v^2} \tag{6.2}$$

$$u\frac{\partial v}{\partial x} + v\frac{\partial v}{\partial y} = \frac{1}{h}\frac{\partial}{\partial x}\left(vh\frac{\partial v}{\partial x}\right) + \frac{1}{h}\frac{\partial}{\partial y}\left(vh\frac{\partial v}{\partial y}\right) - g\frac{\partial Z}{\partial y} - \frac{g}{Kh^{\frac{4}{3}}}v\sqrt{u^2+v^2} \tag{6.3}$$

where

$u, v$     are the horizontal components of the average velocity
$h$        is the depth (given number)
$g$ grad $Z$   is the pressure gradient
$v$        is the momentum diffusion coefficient

Here, friction stresses are expressed by a Strickler coefficient, which generally provides a more accurate picture of depth variations (upper bed–lower bed) than the Chezy coefficient.

It should be noted that if $h(x, y)$, i.e., the integration depth of the Navier–Stokes equations, is given, the pressure gradient is not defined. Equations (6.1), (6.2) and (6.3) obtained by this method are very similar to the Navier–Stokes two-dimensional equations. Since the momentum equations are not linear, an iterative solution process must be defined. As this non-linear feature characterizes convection terms, it seemed of interest to re-introduce a 'time' derivative of the velocity into the momentum equations. The velocity field is determined under stationary conditions. With the process proposed here, the algorithms described above can be used.

### 6.2.2  Curvilinear grid

The main modification consists in introducing a curvilinear grid and solving the equations within this grid. The principle of the method is based on a change of coordinates which makes it possible to pass from a reference system of any shape, $\Omega$, to a reference system $\hat{\Omega}$ which is either rectangular or easily representable by rectangles.

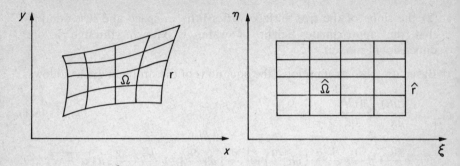

The selected change of coordinates $(x, y)$ to $(\xi, \eta)$ may be that described by Thomson *et al.* (1975), as follows:

$$
\left.
\begin{aligned}
&\frac{\partial^2 \xi}{\partial x^2} + \frac{\partial^2 \xi}{\partial y^2} = 0 \\[6pt]
&\frac{\partial^2 \eta}{\partial x^2} + \frac{\partial^2 \eta}{\partial y^2} = 0 \\[6pt]
&\xi(x\tau, y\tau) = \xi\tau \\[6pt]
&\eta(x\tau, y\tau) = \eta\tau
\end{aligned}
\right\}
\tag{6.4}
$$

where $\tau$ is the boundary of field $\Omega$, and $\xi$ and $\eta$ are the solutions of an elliptic problem which generally provides a regular non-orthogonal grid in plane $(x, y)$. In fact, to solve these equations in a rectangular grid, the previous operator which defines the grid is inverted and the following equations are solved in $\hat{\Omega}$:

$$
\left.
\begin{aligned}
&\alpha \frac{\partial^2 x}{\partial \xi^2} - 2\beta \frac{\partial^2 x}{\partial \xi\, \partial \eta} + \gamma \frac{\partial^2 x}{\partial \eta^2} = 0 \\[6pt]
&\alpha \frac{\partial^2 y}{\partial \xi^2} - 2\beta \frac{\partial^2 y}{\partial \xi\, \partial \eta} + \gamma \frac{\partial^2 y}{\partial \eta^2} = 0
\end{aligned}
\right\}
\tag{6.5}
$$

with $x$ and $y$ given at the boundary and with

$$
\alpha = \left(\frac{\partial x}{\partial \eta}\right)^2 + \left(\frac{\partial y}{\partial \eta}\right)^2
$$

$$
\beta = \frac{\partial x}{\partial \xi} \frac{\partial x}{\partial \eta} + \frac{\partial y}{\partial \xi} \frac{\partial y}{\partial \eta}
$$

$$
\gamma = \left(\frac{\partial x}{\partial \xi}\right)^2 + \left(\frac{\partial y}{\partial \eta}\right)^2 .
$$

These equations are solved using an iterative method (SOR) with finite differences.

Once the grid is completed, the equations are transformed using the change of variables $\xi(x, y)$ and $\eta(x, y)$. The derivatives of all the quantities are transformed as follows:

$$\frac{\partial f}{\partial x}(x, y) = \frac{\partial f}{\partial \xi}\frac{\partial \xi}{\partial x} + \frac{\partial f}{\partial \eta}\frac{\partial \eta}{\partial x}$$

$$\frac{\partial f}{\partial y}(x, y) = \frac{\partial f}{\partial \xi}\frac{\partial \xi}{\partial y} + \frac{\partial f}{\partial \eta}\frac{\partial \eta}{\partial y}.$$

These equations are solved, as in the preceding case, in three stages—convection, diffusion and continuity—as described below.

### 6.2.3  Convection step

Following the change of coordinates, the equations become (using the same incorrect notation as in Section 2.3.3)

$$\frac{\partial u_i}{\partial t} + u_1\left(\frac{\partial u_i}{\partial \xi}\frac{\partial \xi}{\partial x} + \frac{\partial u_i}{\partial \eta}\frac{\partial \eta}{\partial x}\right) + u_2\left(\frac{\partial u_i}{\partial \xi}\frac{\partial \xi}{\partial y} + \frac{\partial u_i}{\partial \eta}\frac{\partial \eta}{\partial y}\right) = 0,$$

giving

$$\frac{\partial u_i}{\partial t} + \left(u_1\frac{\partial \xi}{\partial x} + u_2\frac{\partial \xi}{\partial y}\right)\frac{\partial u_i}{\partial \xi} + \left(u_1\frac{\partial \eta}{\partial x} + u_2\frac{\partial \eta}{\partial y}\right)\frac{\partial u_i}{\partial \eta} = 0 \qquad (6.6)$$

or else, with

$$u' = u_1\frac{\partial \xi}{\partial x} + u_2\frac{\partial \xi}{\partial y}$$

$$v' = u_1\frac{\partial \eta}{\partial x} + u_2\frac{\partial \eta}{\partial y},$$

$$\frac{\partial u_i}{\partial t} + u'\frac{\partial u_i}{\partial \xi} + v'\frac{\partial u_i}{\partial \eta} = 0.$$

Therefore, the convection equation found in plane $\hat{\Omega}$ is of a classical form. The convecting field $(u', v')$ is different from the convected vector $(u, v)$. This equation is solved by the characteristics method described by Daubert (1974).

### 6.2.4  Diffusion step: source term

Following the change of coordinates, the equations of the diffusion step can be written as follows:

$$\frac{\partial u_i}{\partial t} = \frac{1}{h}\frac{\partial}{\partial x}\left[vh\left(\frac{\partial u_i}{\partial \xi}\frac{\partial \xi}{\partial x} + \frac{\partial u_i}{\partial \eta}\frac{\partial \eta}{\partial x}\right)\right]$$

$$+ \frac{1}{h}\frac{\partial}{\partial y}\left[vh\left(\frac{\partial u_i}{\partial \xi}\frac{\partial \xi}{\partial y} + \frac{\partial u_i}{\partial \eta}\frac{\partial \eta}{\partial y}\right)\right] - gu_i\sqrt{u_1^2 + u_2^2}/Kh^{\frac{4}{3}}.$$

By applying again the formula used to change coordinates, the following expression is obtained:

$$\frac{\partial u_i}{\partial t} = \frac{1}{h}\frac{\partial}{\partial \xi}\left[vh\left(\frac{\partial u_i}{\partial \xi}\frac{\partial \xi}{\partial x}+\frac{\partial u_i}{\partial \eta}\frac{\partial \eta}{\partial x}\right)\right]\frac{\partial \xi}{\partial x}+\frac{1}{h}\frac{\partial}{\partial \eta}\left[vh\left(\frac{\partial u_i}{\partial \xi}\frac{\partial \xi}{\partial x}+\frac{\partial u_i}{\partial \eta}\frac{\partial \eta}{\partial x}\right)\right]\frac{\partial \eta}{\partial x}$$

$$+\frac{1}{h}\frac{\partial}{\partial \xi}\left[vh\left(\frac{\partial u_i}{\partial \xi}\frac{\partial \xi}{\partial y}+\frac{\partial u_i}{\partial \eta}\frac{\partial \eta}{\partial y}\right)\right]\frac{\partial \xi}{\partial y}+\frac{1}{h}\frac{\partial}{\partial \eta}\left[vh\left(\frac{\partial u_i}{\partial \xi}\frac{\partial \xi}{\partial y}+\frac{\partial u_i}{\partial \eta}\frac{\partial \eta}{\partial y}\right)\right]\frac{\partial \eta}{\partial y}$$

$$-gu_i\sqrt{u_1^2+u_2^2}/Kh^{\frac{4}{3}}. \tag{6.7}$$

These equations are described in finite differences, in a classical way, and the velocity components are calculated at the same point. The discretization process is detailed in the work of Keramsi (1978) and Mary (in preparation). The discretized equations are solved, in a very classical way, by over-relaxation. The components of the velocity field obtained at the end of these two steps are denoted by $u_i^{aux}$.

### 6.2.5 Continuity step

The continuity equation must now be taken into account and the following equations must be solved:

$$\left.\begin{array}{l}\dfrac{\partial u_i}{\partial t}=-g\dfrac{\partial Z}{\partial x_i} \qquad i=1,2 \\[2ex] \dfrac{\partial(u_1 h)}{\partial x_1}+\dfrac{\partial(u_2 h)}{\partial x_2}=0.\end{array}\right\} \tag{6.8}$$

Contrary to what has been said concerning the solution of the Saint-Venant equations, a pressure solution is not sought and the incompressibility relation is suppressed, by using the stream function $\psi$:

$$u_1 h = -\frac{\partial \psi}{\partial x_2}$$

$$u_2 h = \frac{\partial \psi}{\partial x_1}.$$

The stream function is obtained by making the vorticity of the final velocity field identical to that of the field $u^{aux}$. In fact, on considering the vorticity given by Eqs (6.8), one realizes that it must remain identical.

The equation for $\psi$ is

$$\frac{\partial}{\partial x_1}\left(\frac{1}{h}\frac{\partial \psi}{\partial x_1}\right)+\frac{\partial}{\partial x_2}\left(\frac{1}{h}\frac{\partial}{\partial x_2}\psi\right)=\frac{\partial u_2^{aux}}{\partial x_1}-\frac{\partial u_1^{aux}}{\partial x_2}. \tag{6.9}$$

If the two velocity components are given at the boundary of the reference system, $\psi$ and its normal derivative are known. This last equation is solved by using the value of $\psi$ at the boundary. The tangential velocity to be found must be very close to that which is sought if the calculation of vorticity is correct (Viollet *et al.* 1981).

Discretization is performed after Eq. (6.9) has been transformed in plane $(\xi, \eta)$. The $\psi$-grid is overlapped onto the velocity grid and the $\psi$ unknowns are calculated at the centre of the velocity meshes. The discretization of Eq. (6.9) is such that it is consistent with that relating the current function to velocity, and with that relating vorticity to the velocity components. This aspect is of particular importance, since experience has proved that if this condition were not met, a noticeable error would appear in the velocity component tangential to the side (river bank), which, in some cases, might have a serious impact on the whole flow. Equation (6.9) is solved by over-relaxation.

A similar operator might be solved under Neumann boundary conditions (Section 2.3) in order to determine the pressure field. A further iteration on the elevation of the water surface would enable the results to be refined.

### 6.2.6 Results

As a preliminary illustration, an attempt was made to apply this model to a case in which the results to be obtained would be comparable with those gained from measurements. A study, using a scale model, was carried out for part of the River Aube. In this rather complex geometry, the velocity field was known.

The studied area, about 380 m long, is contained within a rectangle 350 m long and 110 m wide. The average slope of the river bed is of the order of $2 \times 10^{-3}$. The river bed is V-shaped and rather irregular. The slope of the banks ranges from 0.5/1 to 6/1, with an average of about 3/1. The radii of curvature of the two bends are about 120 m. The average depth is of the order of 4 m. Figure 6.2 shows two maps of the river bed. The lower map was plotted from the values recorded at the nodes.

In this section of the River Aube, the flow is rapid and the average Froude number is about 0.7. The two bends induce significant secondary currents, resulting in surface elevations of more than 0.15 m. Measurements of the average velocities were carried out on a vertical using a

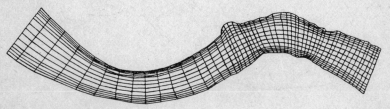

*Fig. 6.1*   Grid applied to the River Aube

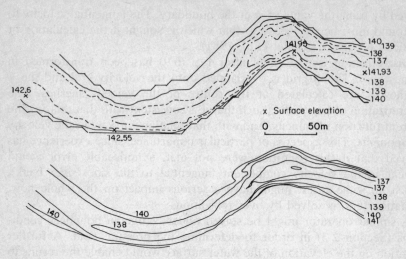

*Fig. 6.2*   Plots of the river-bed elevations

Beauvert current-meter in order to define the cross-section of the velocities in several sections of the river.

The studied part of the river includes two successive bends, and the grid pattern used is shown in Fig. 6.1. It is tighter in the vicinity of the banks in order to allow for the very substantial velocity gradient near the banks. The number of points is about 800. The calculations were carried out under the assumption that the free surface is horizontal, with a Strickler coefficient of 60 and a constant viscosity of 5 m²/s. A variation in this parameter showed that viscosity had a noticeable impact on flow. The chosen value of 5 m²/s is that which provided the best comparison with the measurements.

Figure 6.3 is a comparison between the measured and calculated profiles, and the correlation is fairly satisfactory. The observed differences

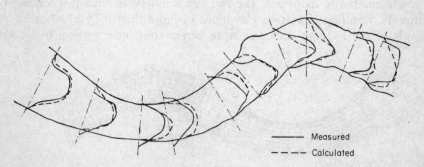

*Fig. 6.3*   Comparison of the measured and calculated velocity profiles

may be due, on the one hand, to the three-dimensional nature of the flow, which is not represented, and, on the other hand, to the difficulty of defining, with accuracy, the exact limits of the river.

This is only a preliminary application, but the results can be considered as promising and this model seems better adapted to river flows than the traditional Saint-Venant model. The solution of the pressure field may make it possible to carry out iterations in order to determine the location of the free surface. The solution of the concentration field will facilitate the study of certain pollution problems requiring a two-dimensional approach.

## 6.3 Three-dimensional model

The type of model described can be used to study the pollution problems in remote or medium-distance fields. However, owing to its two-dimensionality, it does not make it possible to study the immediate vicinity of an outfall. In that case, a specific method must be used, which involves solving the three-dimensional Navier–Stokes equations, combined with a temperature equation. The method used to solve the equations is derived from those already described in previous chapters and it will not be recalled here. A detailed description of this method has been given by Esposito (1979).

Let us recall only that thermal diffusion was defined by means of an anisotropic diffusion coefficient which made it possible to represent the reduction of vertical transfers resulting from the turbulence damping action of gravity forces. The diffusion pattern selected in the horizontal plane is identical to that described by Viollet (1979). This very simple model is a first approach and should not be considered as a final stage.

This model was applied to the case of a hot fluid discharged in a cross-flow at the surface of a test flume. The results were compared with measurements. The following values were used:

| | |
|---|---|
| Densimetric Froude number | 8 |
| Reynolds number | 20 000 |
| Difference between temperature at the outfall point and ambient temperature, $T_0$ | 17°C |
| Velocity in the flume, $V$ | 11.6 cm/s |
| Velocity in the evacuated fluid | 24.4 cm/s |
| Flume height | 12.5 cm |
| Flume width, $B$ | 60 cm |
| Height of evacuated fluid, $a$ | 2.5 cm |
| Width of evacuated fluid, $b$ | 5 cm |

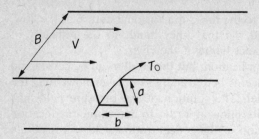

The calculation was performed using the two calculation grids (fine and coarse) shown on Fig. 6.6. Figure 6.4 describes the surface-velocity field in the fine grid. A recirculation can be observed under the jet. This is partly due to water flowing under the discharged fluid. It can be seen that the divergence of the velocity field in the plane is not zero. It appears that the width, $l$, of this recirculating fluid was perfectly in accordance with the widths mentioned in the corresponding literature (Fig. 6.5). In this case, the three-dimensional nature of the velocity field is not due to gravity effects, since the Froude number is relatively large. It is only due to the fact that the discharged fluid is not distributed over the entire depth.

Figure 6.8 provides a comparison, between measurements and calculations, of the decrease of temperature along the jet axis. The correlation is fairly good. However, an examination (Figs 6.6 and 6.7) of the surface-temperature field in the coarse and fine grids shows a rather substantial difference between the measurements and the calculations. This is mainly because the calculations exaggerate the deflection of the jet by the current. Since the calculated width of the recirculated fluid is closer to that found in the literature than the experimental one, the difference can be explained by a non-uniform upstream velocity profile. In fact, the jet

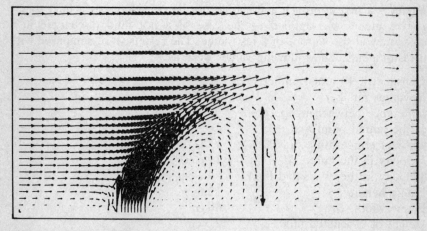

*Fig. 6.4*   Velocity field in fine grid

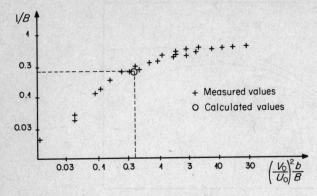

*Fig. 6.5* Recirculation width (from Mikhail)

could obviously be influenced by modifying the profile of the upstream velocity. Unfortunately, we cannot rely on accurate upstream velocity measurements.

Beyond a certain distance from the outfall, even if substantial variations can be observed in the vertical plane, it becomes possible to use a different three-dimensional model which makes the solution much easier. This model is not described here but in Chapter 9 in the context of the study of atmospheric plumes.

This example shows that, in some cases, a three-dimensional code can be used to analyze the field in the vicinity of a river outfall. However, it should be noted that it is applicable just as it is only in cases where the geometry is relatively simple and that a more sophisticated turbulence simulation must be developed to represent the impact of density on the reduction in mixing. The problems raised by the upstream motion of hot

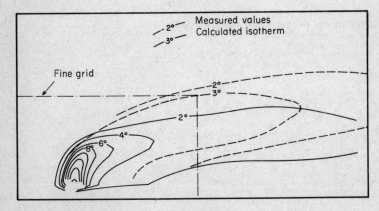

*Fig. 6.6* Thermal field in coarse grid

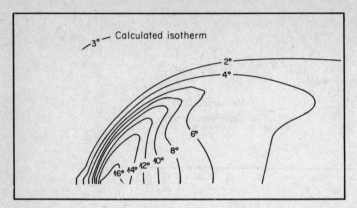

*Fig. 6.7*   Thermal field in fine grid

water (hot intrusion phenomenon), which is very important for the operation of a power station, could then be examined.

This code, which is entirely three-dimensional, has found little application in the environmental field since, in many cases, a summary description of flow is sufficient. By contrast, it has been used more intensively in industrial hydraulics.

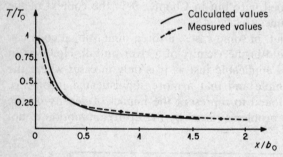

*Fig. 6.8*   Temperature profile along the jet axis

# Part 3 The atmosphere

# 7  Introduction

## 7.1  Various scales of atmospheric movement

Flow in the atmosphere is substantially influenced by

(a) the Coriolis acceleration;
(b) the impact of inertia, as a result of the relief of the Earth's surface or convection phenomena.

The relative magnitude of these factors can be assessed through the Rossby number,

$$Ro = \frac{V}{fL},$$

where $V$ and $L$ represent, respectively, the velocity and the length which characterize the flow to be studied, and $f$ is the Coriolis parameter, defined as follows:

$$f = 2\Omega \sin \lambda,$$

where $\lambda$ is the latitude, and $\Omega$ the rotational angular velocity of the Earth.

Since the velocity scale is always of the order of 10 m/s, the flows can be classified in relation to the length scale:

(a) $Ro \ll 1$, $L > 1000$ km. This is the *synoptic scale* that corresponds to the major meteorological phenomena. The impact of inertia is negligible and the flow results from the equilibrium between pressure and Coriolis forces: this *geostrophic* flow, which is typical of the highest atmospheric layers, is defined by the following system:

$$-\frac{1}{\rho}\frac{\partial P}{\partial x} + fV_{\mathrm{g}} = 0$$

$$-\frac{1}{\rho}\frac{\partial P}{\partial x} - fU_{\mathrm{g}} = 0.$$

(b) $Ro \simeq 1$, $L \simeq 100$ km. This is the *mesoscale*, also referred to as the medium scale. Inertial and Coriolis forces are of the same order, and they cannot be neglected. This is the scale concerned in the study of the atmospheric boundary layer which, as shown by the Ekman model, is characterized by a strong rotational motion at the highest altitudes. This scale also appears in the study of flow at the regional level.

(c) $Ro \gg 1$, $L < 10$ km. This is the *microscale*, at which local phenomena occur—the near field for dilution of an effluent, which will be influenced mainly by the jet or convective plume effects. The impact of Coriolis acceleration is negligible.

For the purpose of this classification, interesting information can be derived from the study of the energy spectrum of velocity fluctuations in the atmosphere (see Fig. 7.1). Substantial energies are developed by movements with periods of between 10 and 100 h, i.e., diurnal movements associated with the synoptic scale. Substantial energies can also be observed when the period is about 1 min. These are turbulent fluctuations which correspond to the microscale. The mesoscale is characterized by a relatively low-energy density of velocity fluctuations, with periods ranging from about 10 min to 1 h. It will therefore be advisable to define average values and to integrate over such time intervals.

Neither the synoptic scale nor the major meteorological perturbations will be analyzed in this work, which bears on the dispersal of pollutants. We shall now proceed with the description of a model used for pollutant follow-up purposes at the regional scale (mesoscale), before concentrating on the jet-induced dilution of pollutants in the near field.

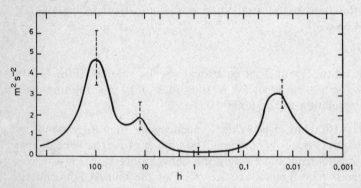

*Fig. 7.1* Spectral distribution of turbulent energy in the vicinity of the ground (from Van der Hoven 1957)

# 8 Mesoscale model

## 8.1 Phenomenon modelling

The model described here (Dewagenaere 1979) is aimed at enabling the spread of a pollutant to be followed, at the regional level, over distances of a few hundreds of kilometres. It can also make it possible to interpolate the meteorological conditions at a given site from the data provided by the measurement network of the Office National Météorologique, which, as a matter of fact, is not very dense. Consequently, one is concerned here with the mesoscale, which means that the main factors having an impact on the flow are:

(a) the relief characteristics;
(b) the Coriolis acceleration (the Rossby number is about 1).

Some thermal effects, e.g., the inversion of the synoptic temperatures, must be taken into account. The thermal effects related to the diurnal cycle (inversion of the morning temperatures, valley breezes, etc) are not studied at present, but they can be represented by the model through a special modelling of the heat transfers in the vicinity of the ground.

### 8.1.1 Flow dynamics assumptions

The vertical extension of the phenomena is assumed to be small. The vertical component of velocity is small, compared with the horizontal components. Therefore, the pressure can be considered as hydrostatic. This assumption is justified by the small slope of natural relief, for which the horizontal length scale is noticeably larger than the vertical length scale. However, it excludes all the major convective phenomena which occur under unstable atmospheric conditions which are characterized by high vertical velocities (e.g., the formation of cumuli). It should be noted that these phenomena could be studied in the absence of relief.

The Mach number, i.e., the ratio of the typical velocity involved to the velocity of sound, is low (about 0.1 with a wind speed of 30 m/s), which makes it possible to disregard the variations of the density in the continuity equation. The problem is thus reduced to that of an incompressible fluid. By introducing the two quantities

$$\pi = C_p \left( \frac{P}{P_0} \right)^{R/C_p} \qquad \text{(Exner pressure)}$$

and

$$\theta = T \left( \frac{P_0}{P} \right)^{R/C_p} \qquad \text{(potential temperature)},$$

which is a classical method in meteorology (Charney 1973), the equations of the problem are as follows:

$$\frac{\partial u}{\partial t} + u \frac{\partial u}{\partial x} + v \frac{\partial u}{\partial y} + w \frac{\partial u}{\partial z}$$

$$= -\theta \frac{\partial \pi}{\partial x} + fv + \frac{\partial}{\partial x} \left( \nu_h \frac{\partial u}{\partial x} \right) + \frac{\partial}{\partial y} \left( \nu_h \frac{\partial u}{\partial y} \right) + \frac{\partial}{\partial z} \left( \nu_z \frac{\partial u}{\partial z} \right),$$

$$\frac{\partial v}{\partial t} + u \frac{\partial v}{\partial x} + v \frac{\partial v}{\partial y} + w \frac{\partial v}{\partial z}$$

$$= -\theta \frac{\partial \pi}{\partial y} - fu + \frac{\partial}{\partial x} \left( \nu_h \frac{\partial v}{\partial x} \right) + \frac{\partial}{\partial y} \left( \nu_h \frac{\partial v}{\partial y} \right) + \frac{\partial}{\partial z} \left( \nu_z \frac{\partial v}{\partial z} \right),$$

$$0 = -\theta \frac{\partial \pi}{\partial z} - g$$

$$\frac{\partial u}{\partial x} + \frac{\partial v}{\partial y} + \frac{\partial w}{\partial z} = 0,$$

$$\frac{\partial \theta}{\partial t} + u \frac{\partial \theta}{\partial x} + v \frac{\partial \theta}{\partial y} + w \frac{\partial \theta}{\partial z} = \frac{\partial}{\partial x} \left( \kappa_h \frac{\partial \theta}{\partial x} \right) + \frac{\partial}{\partial z} \left( \kappa_h \frac{\partial \theta}{\partial z} \right) + \frac{\partial}{\partial z} \left( \kappa_z \frac{\partial \theta}{\partial z} \right).$$

In this system, $u$ and $v$ are the horizontal components of velocity (in $x$ and $y$), and $w$ is the vertical component. The turbulent transfers are represented by the horizontal coefficients $\nu_h$, $\kappa_h$ and by the vertical coefficients $\nu_z$ and $\kappa_z$. The modelling of this is described later.

Apart from temperature, this system is identical to that obtained in the three-dimensional sea-current problem (see Section 4.1).

### 8.1.2 Boundary conditions

*At ground level*
The flow of the wind above the ground is, in virtually all cases, a rough turbulent flow. The surface layer and the roughness length scale are very small, compared with the size of the meshes near the ground. The

dynamic condition must then be expressed as follows:

$$v_z \frac{\partial U}{\partial z} = u_*^2$$

The ratio of the friction velocity, $u_*$, to the geostrophic wind velocity, $u_g$, depends on surface roughness (a value of about $5 \times 10^{-2}$ is generally found in the atmosphere). In the present model, the boundary condition for the temperature is simply $\partial \theta / \partial z = 0$.

*In altitude*
The calculation field is necessarily limited in the direction of altitude. Therefore, one should admit that the influence of relief can be felt only within a given altitude limit. The connection of flow in the lower layers, as described in the model, to the geostrophic flow is achieved through a fluid surface which is assumed to be at constant pressure. This surface, which is thus similar to the free surface of a water flow, is supposed to be located at a sufficient altitude for relief-induced deformations to be small.

The conditions are therefore those of a classical free surface, with a constant pressure and

$$\frac{\partial u}{\partial z} = \frac{\partial v}{\partial z} = \frac{\partial \theta}{\partial z} = 0,$$

as well as $w = dS/dt$, where $S(x, y, t)$ is the altitude of the free surface.

*On the vertical boundaries*
In the absence of measurements, modelling is required. The relief is supposed to be flat at the boundaries and, with the exception of pressure, the flow parameters are homogeneous in the horizontal direction. The horizontal velocities can then be determined through a generalization of the Ekman model, as already described for the sea boundary layer (see Section 4.1), but with only one difference: in the sea, the mass current is known, while in the atmosphere, only the geostrophic wind is assumed to be known.

The temperature profile is given as an assumption when the flow is entering the computing field. It is assumed to be adiabatic on the other parts of the boundary.

### 8.1.3 Turbulence modelling

*Horizontal transfers*
In our problem, the horizontal gradients are very small, compared with the vertical gradients. Therefore, in the model, the horizontal diffusion is represented by a constant mixing length, as in sea problems (see Chapter 4).

*Vertical transfers*

Conversely, the vertical transfers require an accurate model, as a result of the substantial frictional forces and interference with thermal phenomena. Moreover, it is not desirable to increase the complexity of the system to be solved by introducing additional multidimensional differential equations. Consequently, a compromise is chosen, as follows.

The equations used to describe the correlations to be calculated, $\overline{u_i'u_j'}$ and $\overline{u_i'T'}$ ($i$ and $j = 1$ to 3 for $x$, $y$, $z$), as well as the turbulent energy, $k = \frac{1}{2}(\overline{u'^2} + \overline{v'^2} + \overline{w'^2})$, and $\overline{T'^2}$, are described through the Launder (1975) model for unknown terms. Dissipation, $\varepsilon$, is then modelled as follows:

$$\varepsilon = C_E \frac{k^{1.5}}{l},$$

where $C_E = 0.47$ and $l$ is a length scale to be specified in the assumptions. The horizontal gradients are assumed to be negligible, compared with the vertical gradients. Moreover, the classical local equilibrium assumption is adopted: the energy produced is assumed to be instantaneously absorbed or dissipated at the same place, and therefore the diffusion, transport and unsteady terms are not taken into account.

The following equations are obtained (with $i$ and $j = 1$ and 2 for the horizontal, 3 for the vertical, and $\alpha$ and $\beta = 1$ to 2 for the horizontal directions):

$$\overline{u_3'u_i'}\frac{\partial U_\alpha}{\partial x_3}\delta_{j3} + \overline{u_3'u_j'}\frac{\partial U_\alpha}{\partial x_3}\delta_{i\alpha} + \frac{C_m k^{\frac{1}{2}}}{l}(\overline{u_i'u_j'} - \tfrac{2}{3}k) + \frac{C_E k^{\frac{1}{2}}}{l}\overline{u_i'u_j'}$$

$$- C_r k\left(\frac{\partial U_\beta}{\partial x_3}\delta_{j3}\delta_{i\beta} + \frac{\partial U_\beta}{\partial x_3}\delta_{i3}\delta_{j\beta}\right) + \frac{g}{T_0}(\overline{T'u_i'}\delta_{j3} + \overline{T'u_j'}\delta_{i3}) = 0$$

$$\overline{T'u_3'}\frac{\partial U_\alpha}{\partial x_3}\delta_{i\alpha} + \overline{u_i'u_3'}\frac{\partial T}{\partial x_3} + \frac{\beta k^{\frac{1}{2}}}{l}\overline{T'u_i'} + \tfrac{2}{3}\overline{T'^2}\delta_{i3}\frac{g}{T_0} + \frac{C_s k^{\frac{1}{2}}}{l}\overline{u_i'T'} = 0$$

$$2\overline{T'u_3'}\frac{\partial T}{\partial x_3} + \frac{C_\theta k^{\frac{1}{2}}}{l}\overline{T'^2} = 0,$$

where $\delta_{ij}$ is the Kronecker symbol ($\delta_{ij} = 1$ if $i = j$ and $\delta_{ij} = 0$ if $i \neq j$). Likewise, the fluctuations of velocity with respect to its average value $U_i$ are denoted by $u_i'$, in the usual way, and the fluctuations of temperature with respect to its average value, $T$, are denoted by $T'$. The bar above a term means that the average value of this term is used. The constants are $C_m = 0.7$; $C_r = 0.4$; $C_\theta = 0.35$; $\beta + C_s = 1.77$.

It can be shown (Dewagenaere 1979) that eddy viscosity and diffusivity coefficients, $\nu_z$ and $\kappa_z$, can be determined from this system, which can be solved algebraically. If the length scale, $l$, is expressed in a classical manner, i.e., with $l = 1.3z$ in the neutral case, the value of the Kármán constant (0.4) is found.

The impact of thermal phenomena on turbulence is included in this model in a natural way. Figure 8.1 shows the variations of turbulent energy as a function of the Richardson number:

$$Ri = \frac{\dfrac{g}{T}\dfrac{\partial T}{\partial z}}{\left(\dfrac{\partial u}{\partial z}\right)^2 + \left(\dfrac{\partial v}{\partial z}\right)^2}.$$

In a stable medium $(Ri > 0)$, the energy decreases rapidly, and falls to zero when $Ri = 0.4$.

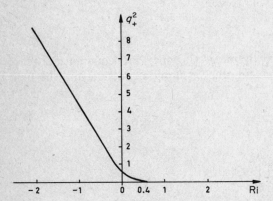

*Fig. 8.1* Non-dimensional turbulent kinetic energy, $q_+^2$

## 8.2 Numerical solution

In the problem to be solved, the relief exerts its influence through the boundaries of the integration field of the system. The selected method consists in reducing the calculation field to a parallelepiped, by means of a variable change on the vertical coordinate.

If $z_F(x, y)$ is the elevation of the ground and $S(x, y, t)$ the elevation of the free surface, the following expression can be written:

$$z^* = \bar{S}\frac{z - z_F}{S - z_F}, \quad 0 \leq z^* \leq \bar{S},$$

where $\bar{S} = S(x, y, 0)$ is the initial elevation of the free surface, which is assumed to be horizontal. This method makes the description of the integration field noticeably easier but it also involves the solution of more complex equations.

The breakdown into the various steps is identical to that described in Section 4.2. The solution of the convection–diffusion stages is unchanged, and temperature is calculated by the same methods. However, the solution of the pressure-continuity stage is more difficult than that described in Section 4.2.3, since the potential temperature, $\theta$, is not constant. In fact, the equations of the atmospheric problem, which correspond to Eqs (4.18), (4.19) and (4.20), are:

$$\frac{u^{n+1}-u^{(2)}}{\mathrm{d}t} = -\theta\frac{\partial\pi^{n+1}}{\partial x} - g\frac{z^*}{S}\frac{\partial S^{n+1}}{\partial x} - g\frac{\bar{S}-z^*}{\bar{S}}\frac{\partial z_F}{\partial x},$$

$$\frac{v^{n+1}-v^{(2)}}{\mathrm{d}t} = -\theta\frac{\partial\pi^{n+1}}{\partial y} - g\frac{z^*}{S}\frac{\partial S^{n+1}}{\partial y} - g\frac{\bar{S}-z^*}{\bar{S}}\frac{\partial z_F}{\partial y},$$

$$\theta\frac{\partial\pi^{n+1}}{\partial z^*} = -g\frac{S^{n+1}-z_F}{\bar{S}}.$$

Pressure must be suppressed by integrating the third equation between $z^* = 0$ and $z^* = \bar{S}$ and introducing the resulting expression into the first two equations. With

$$H = S - z_F$$

and

$$U = \int_{z_F}^{S(x,y,t)} u\,\mathrm{d}z = \frac{S-z_F}{\bar{S}}\int_0^{\bar{S}} u\,\mathrm{d}z^*,$$

the following system is obtained:

$$\frac{1}{H^{n+1}}\frac{U^{n+1}-U^{(2)}}{\mathrm{d}t} = \left(-\frac{g}{\bar{S}^2}A - \frac{g}{2}\right)\frac{\partial H^{n+1}}{\partial x} + \frac{g}{\bar{S}^2}B_x H^{n+1} - g\frac{\partial z_F}{\partial x}$$

$$\frac{1}{H^{n+1}}\frac{V^{n+1}-V^{(2)}}{\mathrm{d}t} = \left(-\frac{g}{\bar{S}^2}A - \frac{g}{2}\right)\frac{\partial H^{n+1}}{\partial y} + \frac{g}{\bar{S}^2}B_y H^{n+1} - g\frac{\partial z_F}{\partial y}$$

$$\frac{H^{n+1}-H^n}{\mathrm{d}t} = -\left(\frac{\partial U^{n+1}}{\partial x} + \frac{\partial V^{n+1}}{\partial y}\right)$$

where $A$, $B_x$ and $B_y$ are integral expressions of $\theta$, $\partial\theta/\partial x$, $\partial\theta/\partial y$.

This hyperbolic system may be solved by introducing fractionary steps, enabling the two directions to be segregated: the two systems are subsequently linearized and discretized so that they can be solved.

## 8.3 Application to the Alsace Plain

When the wind blows from the west, the Alsace Plain is supplied by the Paris Basin, which is relatively flat. Therefore, this case lends itself to the utilization of models.

### 8.3.1 Comparison with an experiment on a scale model under neutral atmospheric conditions

The experiments were carried out on a scale model representing the Alsace Plain, the Vosges Mountains and the Black Forest. This model was placed in the 8 m long by 2 m wide flume of the rotating platform of the Grenoble Mechanics Institute. In the vertical direction, the scale was $1:25\,000$; in the horizontal direction, it was $1:110\,000$. The depth of water was 0.16 m. The calculations represent the same region, with the same distortion as the scale model. Figure 8.2 describes the grid at elevation $z^* = 0$. The number of points in the vertical direction is 15.

A test without rotation enables the friction coefficients to be adjusted in the numerical model. This adjustment, typical of the scale model, is made necessary by the low Reynolds number of the experiment, which, to a certain extent, is offset by a high surface roughness and by distortion, which favours separation. The macroscale, $l$, is still chosen proportional to the altitude up to a given value. Within the scope of an application to the real atmosphere, the proportionality constant would be the same everywhere. However, in the representation of the experiment, it has been proved necessary to increase the value of the proportionality constant whenever a relief is encountered.

For the purpose of the experiment, the following expression was determined:

$$l = 1.3(1 + \alpha z_F)(z - z_F),$$

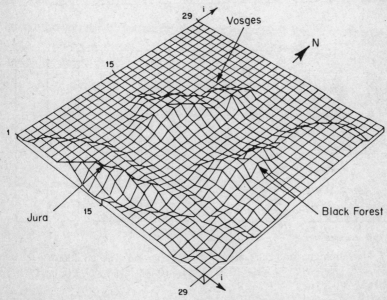

*Fig. 8.2* Relief of the area. Horizontal grid: 8 km × 8 km. Distorted vertical scale

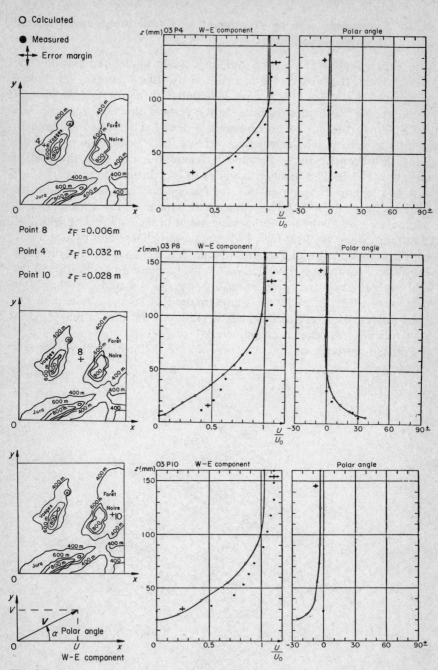

Fig. 8.3 Measurements and calculations without rotation. Test conditions: $R_0 \to \infty$; $F_r^2 = 0.025$; $Re_2 = 10^4$; $\delta = 4 \times 10^{-2}$; $\lambda = 1/110\,000$; $(U_{am}/G) \# (z/0.045)^{0.25}$; $H = 0.16$ m; $V \# 0.20$ m/s

where $\alpha$ is the ratio of the vertical scale to the horizontal scale of the flow (this parameter characterizes the slope of the reliefs, hence it is about four times greater in the experiment than in reality).

The calculations carried out in the experiment with rotation are based on the same friction law. For both cases, comparisons between the calculations and the experimental results are shown in Figs 8.3 and 8.4, corresponding to three points (4, 8 and 10) which are representative of a E–W profile. (More detailed results can be found in Dewagenaere's study (1979).)

Without rotation, the channelling effect can be felt only in the middle of the Plain, where a pronounced slowing down occurs under the action of the wind from the Vosges summits, resulting in the formation of a turbulent wake. With rotation, the channelling effect, still strengthened by the Coriolis forces, is much more substantial.

The calculations determine, with a good accuracy, the deflection of the flow by the relief and by Coriolis acceleration, as well as the general characteristics of the air flow to the Alsace Plain. The accuracy is less satisfactory as regards the velocities. The observed differences are due to the following factors:

(a) The scale-model distortion results in a slight separation downstream from the Vosges, a phenomenon which cannot be reproduced by calculations, owing to the assumption of hydrostatic pressure.
(b) Due to the low Reynolds number in the experiment, as well as to the lateral containment, it is impossible to obtain a good description of the boundary of the rotating atmosphere upstream of the surveyed area.

### 8.3.2 Study of a stratified atmosphere

The thermal stratification, which may appear during periods of one to several days, stops the turbulent transfers in the vertical direction (see Fig. 8.1), exerting a drawback force on the upwards movements generated by relief: this is the 'lid effect'. As an example, we cite the case of a very severe temperature inversion (19° between altitudes of 1000 and 1500 m) covering the Vosges Mountains and the Black Forest, with a westerly geostrophic wind having a velocity of 5 m/s. This represents a rather pronounced inversion in reality.

The results of these calculations are shown on Figs 8.5 and 8.6. Pronounced wind accelerations can be observed, especially to the south of the Alsace Plain and to the north-west of the Vosges Mountains. The northern part of the Plain is relatively calm, which is an obvious demonstration of the 'lid effect'.

The classical relief-induced wave phenomena are shown in the calculations. Moreover, an overall decrease and a weakening of the inversion can be noted in the Plain.

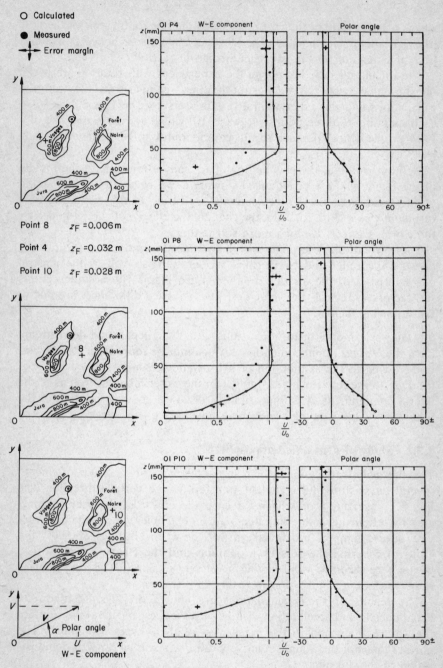

*Fig. 8.4* Measurements and calculations with rotation. Test conditions: $R_0 = 2.3$; $F_r^2 = 0.025$; $Re_2 = 10^4$; $\delta = 4 \times 10^{-2}$; $\lambda = 1/110\,000$; $(U_{am}/G)\#(z/0.045)^{0.25}$; $H = 0.16$ m; $V\#0.20$ m/s

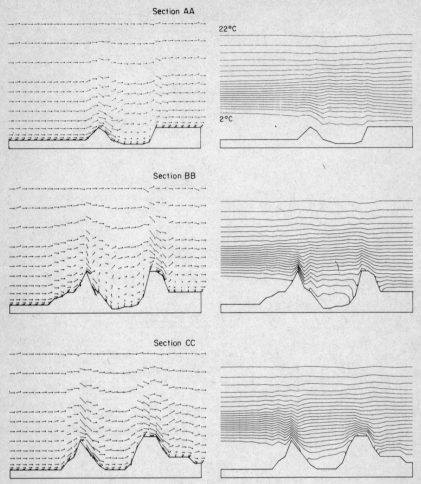

*Fig. 8.5* Zonal sections of velocity and temperature fields for 19° inversion between 1000 and 1500 m. The isotherms presented are spaced at intervals of 1°. Horizontal scale: 1 cm ≈ 45 km; vertical scale: 1 cm ≈ 900 m

## 8.4 Conclusion—Use of and prospects for developing the model

In its present form, the model can be used for pollutant follow-up purposes on a regional scale. However, efforts will have to be made in order to achieve a satisfactory modelling of the pollutant source. A near-field model is described in the following chapter but the transfer function between the two models remains to be defined in a judicious way.

Under non-isothermal conditions, the model seems to provide a fairly good description of the interactions between a synoptic inversion affecting

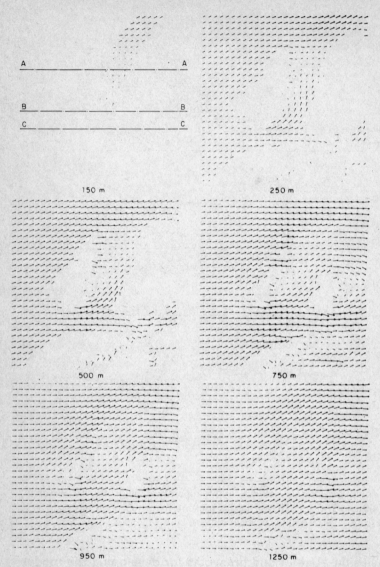

*Fig. 8.6* Geostrophic wind from the west. Velocity field sections for 19° inversion between 1000 and 1500 m

a region, and the relief of the region. This interaction between the three-dimensional relief effect and stratification will be checked through experiments without rotation, using a hydraulic flume, in which inversion is simulated by upstream injection of a hot layer above the cold layer.

Local thermal effects related to the diurnal cycle (valley breezes, low-layer inversions) will be represented when a more accurate model of thermal conditions at ground level, and especially of radiations, has been found.

# 9 Small-scale modelling of discharges into the atmosphere: cooling-tower plumes

## 9.1 Model selection

### 9.1.1 Constraints and basic options

It should be recalled that the field covered by the model is defined by the two following conditions:

(1) The length scale involved is the microscale, which makes it possible to disregard the Coriolis acceleration and to assume that the meteorological conditions are stationary and homogeneous in the horizontal direction.
(2) The dynamics specifically induced by the discharge, through the jet or convective-plume effects, generates a turbulence which is sufficiently severe for the atmospheric boundary-layer turbulence to play a minor role in the mixing process.

In the case examined here, i.e., the release of hot air and steam from the cooling-towers of power stations, the extent of this field was estimated at about 10 km.

The receiving atmosphere is heterogeneous in the vertical direction, from the standpoint of flow velocity, temperature and moisture content, showing variations which can be sudden in the presence of a temperature inversion. Therefore, the studied phenomenon will, very likely, be entirely three-dimensional.

Due to the relatively large size of the area surveyed (compared with the initial size of the plume), attention should be paid to consistency between the calculation costs and the amount of use the model will get for industrial purposes. A lot of so-called 'integral models' (the first of which was probably that of Fan (1967)) exist, implying Gauss-type distribution, symmetrical with respect to the plume axis. They solve balance equations, using empirical hydraulic drag and entrainment coefficients. However, the forecasts which can be made through these interpolation tools are very limited, since the adjustment coefficients are not universal and the model assumptions are too restrictive.

The option chosen by the Laboratoire National d'Hydraulique consists in using the local three-dimensional equations of the problem, after simplifying them as much as possible to make the calculations easier yet without diminishing the three-dimensional nature of the phenomenon. If necessary, an entirely three-dimensional solution may be used locally.

### 9.1.2  Assumptions on the dynamics of the average flow

*No wind*
In the absence of wind, the only simplifying assumption which can be made is that of rotational symmetry about the vertical axis of the plume. The problem is then characterized by two-dimensional equations on cylindrical coordinates, $(r, z)$, the solution of which is relatively easy.

A complex problem arises when account must be taken of the interaction of two or more discharges close to one another. An attempt can be made to set limits within which the solution is comprised, by calculating in sequence a single discharge, then the single discharge equivalent to the set of actual discharges in terms of balance.

*With wind*
See definition diagram in Fig. 9.1. The problem is assumed to be steady-state. In addition, the wind is assumed to be sufficiently strong for the plume to be inclined in such a way that the transverse gradients are predominant compared with the longitudinal gradients (in the wind direction), in which case

(a) the turbulent diffusion in the wind direction is negligible (Taylor assumption);
(b) the pressure gradient in the wind direction is also negligible compared with the transverse gradients and the convective momentum transfers.

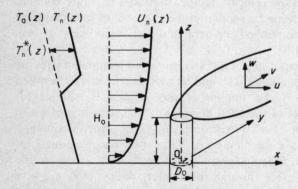

*Fig. 9.1*  Definition diagram

Then, the initial system, which was elliptic, becomes parabolic in $x$, which enables a two-dimensional solution to be found, using successive planes perpendicular to the wind, provided that boundary conditions are defined for each plane and that an initial condition is given for the plane $x = 0$.

$$\frac{\partial u}{\partial x} + \frac{\partial v}{\partial y} + \frac{\partial w}{\partial z} = 0 \tag{9.1}$$

$$\frac{\partial u}{\partial x} + \frac{v}{u}\frac{\partial u}{\partial y} + \frac{w}{u}\frac{\partial u}{\partial z} = \frac{1}{u}\frac{\partial}{\partial y}\left(\nu_h\frac{\partial u}{\partial y}\right) + \frac{1}{u}\frac{\partial}{\partial z}\left(\nu_z\frac{\partial u}{\partial z}\right) \tag{9.2}$$

$$\frac{\partial v}{\partial x} + \frac{v}{u}\frac{\partial v}{\partial y} + \frac{w}{u}\frac{\partial v}{\partial z} = \frac{1}{u}\frac{\partial}{\partial y}\left(\nu_h\frac{\partial v}{\partial y}\right) + \frac{1}{u}\frac{\partial}{\partial z}\left(\nu_h\frac{\partial v}{\partial z}\right) - \frac{1}{\rho_0 u}\frac{\partial P}{\partial y} \tag{9.3}$$

$$\frac{\partial w}{\partial x} + \frac{v}{u}\frac{\partial w}{\partial y} + \frac{w}{u}\frac{\partial w}{\partial z} = \frac{1}{u}\frac{\partial}{\partial y}\left(\nu_h\frac{\partial w}{\partial y}\right) + \frac{1}{u}\frac{\partial}{\partial z}\left(\nu_z\frac{\partial w}{\partial z}\right) - \frac{1}{\rho_0 u}\frac{\partial P}{\partial z} - g\frac{\rho}{\rho_0 u} \tag{9.4}$$

It should be noted that this system was obtained using an asumption on the existence of eddy viscosity coefficients, $\nu_h$ and $\nu_z$, as well as the Boussinesq approximation (see Turner 1973).

### 9.1.3 Water and energy balance assumptions

Even if it is not designed to describe a plume of mist, as in the case of a cooling-tower, a model used to feature the discharge of a substantial quantity of energy into the atmosphere must take account of the evaporation and condensation processes of the water contained under natural conditions in the atmosphere. These processes may indeed have a substantial impact on the energy balance, hence on the dynamics of the problem.

The model currently used, which is based on equilibrium assumptions, is one of the simplest. Let $C$ be the molar fraction of total water (vapour + liquid). The condensed part of the plume is supposed to be concentrated in that area where the relative humidity is 100 per cent. The molar fraction, $C_c$, of condensed water is then determined by the following system:

$$\left. \begin{array}{ll} C_c = C - P_s(T)/P & \text{if } C > P_s(T)/P \\ C_c = 0 \quad \text{(no mist)} & \text{if } C < P_s(T)/P, \end{array} \right\} \tag{9.5}$$

where $P$ is the total pressure (which remains virtually equal to the atmospheric pressure, since $P^*$ is a quantity of the first order) and $P_s(T)$ is the pressure of the saturation vapour at temperature $T$. This amounts to disregarding the dependence of the under-saturation and super-saturation phenomena on the concentration of particles in the air which may become condensation nuclei.

Determining the velocity of particles suspended in a fluid is a very complex problem. Here, we shall assume, very simply, that the droplets are sufficiently small for their velocity to be similar to that of the ambient fluid. This makes it possible to represent the vapour–droplets system by a single contaminant with concentration $C$. This assumption is probably good enough when the diameter of the condensation droplets does not exceed approximately $10 \ \mu\text{m}$. Hence, it is probably realistic when describing the generation of the artificial clouds which are the subject of our study. However, it would not be suitable when studying the evolution of large clouds which might produce rain.

At this stage, it is necessary to take into account the heat quantities related to changes of state in the thermal balance, represented in the average values in Eqs (9.5). Evaporation and condensation are considered as instantaneous, even with respect to turbulent fluctuations. The energy balance, in terms of instantaneous values and using the potential temperature $\theta$, can then be expressed as follows:

$$\frac{d\theta}{dt} = K \Delta\theta + \frac{L_v}{C_p} \frac{M_e}{M_a} \frac{dC_c}{dt}, \tag{9.6}$$

where $L_v$ is the latent heat of evaporation for water, and $M_e$ and $M_a$ are the molar masses of water and air, respectively. In this equation, the instantaneous convection terms which describe both the transfer phenomena induced by the average velocity field and turbulent diffusion, are included in the particle derivative, $d\theta/dt$. This is why the molecular diffusion term, $K\Delta\theta$, can be disregarded, which is the classical approach. Still in terms of instantaneous values, the balance can then be expressed as follows:

$$\left.\begin{aligned}
\frac{dR}{dt} &= 0 \\
\text{where} \quad & \\
R &= \theta - \frac{L_v}{C_p} \frac{M_e}{M_a} C_c.
\end{aligned}\right\} \tag{9.7}$$

That is, if we integrate this equation over time in order again to obtain unknowns in average values (the average value of $R$ being still denoted $R$), we have, under the same assumptions as above,

$$\frac{\partial R}{\partial x} + \frac{v}{u} \frac{\partial R}{\partial y} + \frac{w}{u} \frac{\partial R}{\partial z} = \frac{1}{u} \frac{\partial}{\partial y} \left( \kappa_h \frac{\partial R}{\partial y} \right) + \frac{1}{u} \frac{\partial}{\partial z} \left( \kappa_z \frac{\partial R}{\partial z} \right). \tag{9.8}$$

Water concentration is given by the transport–diffusion equation:

$$\frac{\partial C}{\partial x} + \frac{v}{u} \frac{\partial C}{\partial y} + \frac{w}{u} \frac{\partial C}{\partial z} = \frac{1}{u} \frac{\partial}{\partial y} \left( \nu_h \frac{\partial C}{\partial y} \right) + \frac{1}{u} \frac{\partial}{\partial z} \left( \nu_z \frac{\partial C}{\partial z} \right), \tag{9.9}$$

and the state equation is

$$\frac{\rho^*}{\rho_0} = -\beta(T - T_n) - (C - C_n)\left(1 - \frac{M_e}{M_a}\right),\tag{9.10}$$

where $T_n(z)$ and $C_n(z)$ represent, respectively, the natural temperature and moisture content of the atmosphere undisturbed by the discharge.

### 9.1.4 Turbulence assumptions

The assumptions concerning the existence of eddy viscosity coefficients, $\nu_h$ and $\nu_z$, and eddy diffusivity coefficients, $\kappa_h$ and $\kappa_z$, were already made when Eqs (9.2) (9.3), (9.4), (9.8) and (9.9) were deduced. Based on these assumptions, two methods are available. The first consists in using a turbulence model in order to obtain these coefficients; the model is then made more complex, since additional equations must be solved, but it is also more universal, because no specific adjustment is required. Such two-equation models are beginning to find practical applications and will, very likely, gain currency in the near future. The second method, which has been used by the Laboratoire National d'Hydraulique for plume calculations since 1975, consists in finding simple algebraic expressions for $\nu_h$, $\nu_z$, $\kappa_h$ and $\kappa_z$.

The first assumption is that the following ratios are constant:

$$\frac{\kappa_h}{\nu_h} = \frac{\kappa_z}{\nu_z} = 1.5\tag{9.11}$$

With a neutral or slightly stratified atmosphere, two areas are distinguished:

(1) Within the plume, which is considered as limited by a given concentration of the fluid produced by the cooling-tower, a constant value is chosen: $\kappa_h = \kappa_z = \kappa_T$; its dependence on the significant parameters is studied later.
(2) In the ambient atmosphere, these coefficients depend on altitude and the temperature gradient.

In a severely stratified atmospheric layer, the vertical diffusion coefficient is virtually made equal to zero, in order to allow for the turbulence decrease due to the stabilizing effect of gravity forces. However, from a quantitative viewpoint, it cannot be asserted that the phenomenon is taken into account in a fully satisfactory manner. The calculations show that, from a practical standpoint, the influence of the values assigned to the diffusion coefficients outside the plume are extremely small. Emphasis should thus be laid on the coefficient $\kappa_T$.

For calculations over a radius not exceeding 10 km around the power station—an area which is often referred to as the 'near field'—the

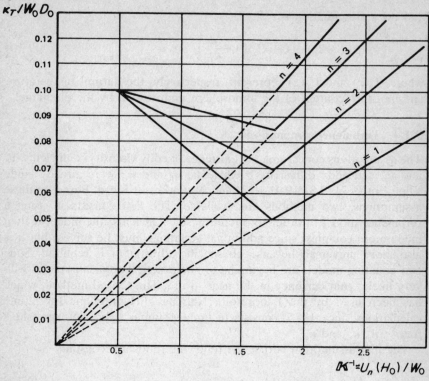

$\kappa_T / W_0 D_0$

$\mathbb{K}^{-1} = U_n (H_0) / W_0$

*Fig. 9.2* Turbulent diffusivity with $0.4 \leq \mathbb{F}_0 \leq 0.8$. (Adjustment for 1 to 4 cooling towers sufficiently spaced apart and forming a square.)

turbulence characteristics depend on the interaction of the jet from the tower and its environment. The impact of such dynamic effects will be examined further, in the light of the results of calculations. Under such conditions, the utilization of flume tests for the calibration or validation of numerical models seems justified. In this way, as many data as required can be obtained and the variations of the significant parameters can be controlled. Generally, similar guarantees are not given by in situ measurements performed with real atmospheric plumes.

From a simplified dimensional analysis, the significant parameters are found to be

$n$ = number of grouped neighbouring cooling-towers

$\mathbb{F}_0 = W_0 / \sqrt{g D_0 \, \Delta\rho/\rho}$, the reduced or densimetric Froude number (where $\Delta\rho/\rho$ represents the relative density variation between the discharged fluid and the ambient atmosphere)

$\mathbb{K} = W_0 / U_n(H_0)$, the ratio of the discharge velocity to the wind velocity at the top of a tower

As regards grouped discharges, spaced at a few diameters, the experi-

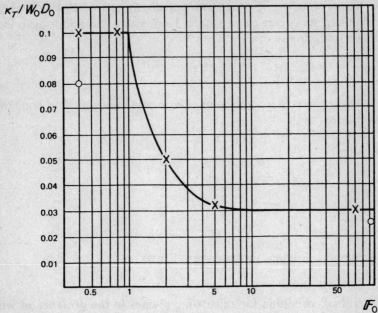

*Fig. 9.3* Turbulent diffusivity with $\mathbb{K} = 2$. ($\circ$ Adjustment for a jet without cross current.)

mental results and their comparison with calculations led to the following results (Viollet 1977):

(a) calm to moderate wind: $\mathbb{K} \geq 2$

$$\kappa_T = \gamma(\mathbb{F}_0) W_0 D_0, \qquad (9.12)$$

where function $\gamma(\mathbb{F}_0)$ is represented on Fig. 9.3;

(b) strong wind: $\mathbb{K} \simeq 0.6$

$$\kappa_T = 0.03 D_0 \sqrt{n} U_n(H_0); \qquad (9.13)$$

(c) when $-0.6 < \mathbb{K} < 2$, there is a linear transition between the two preceding cases (see Fig. 9.2).

## 9.2  Boundary conditions and solution of the system

### 9.2.1  Boundary conditions

The lateral and upper boundaries are determined in order that the influence of the plume could not be felt. Therefore, only a zero-stress condition is imposed on the velocities ($\partial u_i / \partial x_j = 0$ for each velocity $u_i$, where $x_j$ define the direction perpendicular to the surface), and a non-disturbance condition is imposed on the pressure ($P^* = 0$).

The lateral velocity, $V$, is not substantially influenced by the boundary layer phenomena occurring at ground level where the following velocity parameters are imposed:

$$W = 0; \qquad \frac{\partial V}{\partial z} = 0; \qquad \frac{\partial U}{\partial z} = \frac{\partial U_n}{\partial z}.$$

For the four boundaries, the temperature and concentration conditions are as follows:

$$\frac{\partial C}{\partial x_j} = \frac{\partial C_n}{\partial x_j}$$

and

$$\frac{\partial \theta}{\partial x_j} = \frac{\partial \theta_n}{\partial x_j}$$

(the gradients are equal to natural gradients).

### 9.2.2 'Initial' condition for calculating plumes in the presence of wind

The assumptions made in the case where the wind is taken into account, and on the basis of which Eqs (9.2) to (9.4) were defined, are not applicable in the immediate vicinity of the discharge. In this area, it is necessary either to perform a complete three-dimensional computation without making restrictive assumptions, or to use a schematic method.

An example of a complete three-dimensional computation of this type is shown in Fig. 9.4. The solved system is the complete three-dimensional set (without an assumption about the pressure field) of incompressible Navier–Stokes equations. The grid is, of course, coarser in a plane, due to the need for storing all the unknowns at the nodes of the three-dimensional calculation. However, only a complete calculation of this type can provide an accurate representation of flow in the immediate vicinity of the discharge, as well as of the impact of the tower's wake. It should be emphasized that, in this calculation (Benqué and Pernecker 1980), the best result was obtained with the same choice of eddy diffusivities as in the simplified three-dimensional calculation (see Fig. 9.2).

Such a computation can be used to provide the 'initial' condition for a plane-by-plane solution of Eqs (9.1) to (9.4) and (9.8) to (9.10), which makes up the simplified model. However, experience shows that a simple schematization of discharges is sufficient to initiate this calculation. This conservative schematization is now described.

In the plane $x = 0$, the schematization for each discharge consists in introducing a rectangular patch with an area calculated in such a way that the momentum, the thermal capacity and the effluent discharge are exactly represented.

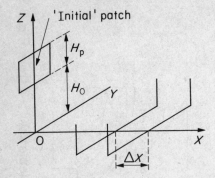

The following conditions are imposed on this plane:

(a) Within the initial patch:

$W = W_0$, discharge velocity
$C = C_0$, discharge concentration
$V = 0$
$\theta = \theta_0$, potential temperature of the discharge
$U = U_n(H_0)/\lambda$, where parameter $\lambda$ characterizes a reduction in the initial longitudinal velocity.

(b) Outside the 'initial' patch:

$V = W = 0; \quad \theta = \theta_n(z); \quad C = C_n(z); \quad U = U_n(z).$

This patch is placed at height $H_0$ (height of the tower) above ground level. Its width is $D_0$ (diameter of the tower), and its height, $H_p$, is given by the following formula:

$$H_p = \frac{\pi}{4} D_0 \lambda \frac{W_0}{U_n(H_0)}. \tag{9.14}$$

The other discharges are introduced in the same manner at each abscissa where they are encountered.

In fact, the weight of parameter $\lambda$ is relatively small, and, in most calculations, $\lambda = 1$. However, when several discharges are combined, this parameter makes it possible to take account of the 'shelter' provided by one discharge for another, when the latter is under the wind of the former.

### 9.2.3 Solution algorithm

The finite-differences solution which is adopted uses the fractionary steps method. Starting from the plane $x = 0$, the equations are solved through

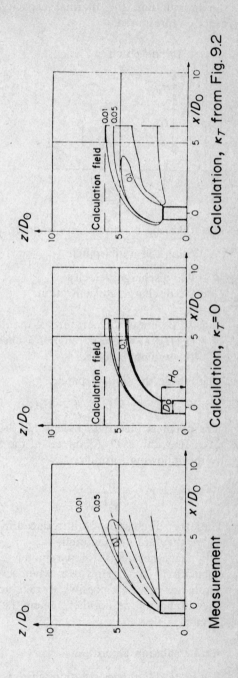

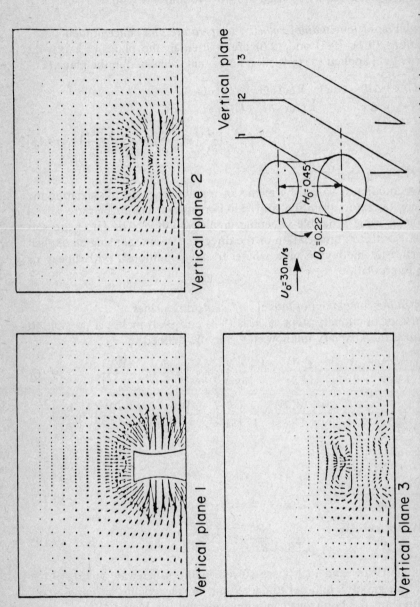

*Fig. 9.4* Complete three-dimensional calculation of flow around a cooling-tower. (*a*) Measurement/calculation comparisons of jet axis and isoconcentrations: $F_0 = 0.8$, $\alpha = 0.25$, $H_0/D_0 = 1.85$; (*b*) velocity fields around the tower

successive planes $(y, z)$ perpendicular to the wind direction, with a rectangular regular grid in each plane. In each of these planes, the grids which are most frequently used are $40 \times 40$ and $120 \times 40$.

*Calculation of longitudinal velocity, temperature and concentration*
Equations (9.1), (9.5) and (9.6) are written in the plane $(x + \Delta x)$, the velocity field applied to convection being that calculated in the plane $(x)$:

$$\frac{G(x + \Delta x) - G(x)}{\Delta x} + \frac{V(x)}{U(x)} \frac{\partial G}{\partial y} + \frac{W(x)}{U(x)} \frac{\partial G}{\partial z}$$

$$= \frac{1}{U(x)} \left[ \frac{\partial}{\partial y} \left( \kappa_h \frac{\partial G}{\partial y} \right) + \frac{\partial}{\partial z} \left( \kappa_z \frac{\partial G}{\partial z} \right) \right] \quad (9.15)$$

with $G = u$, $\theta$, then $C$.

This equation is solved by means of fractionary steps, dissociating the diffusion operators from the convection operators. The former are solved separately using a double-sweeping implicit method. The latter are solved, still with the dissociation of the directions y and z, using an explicit characteristic method (stable whatever the conditions), with linear or cubic interpolation.

*Intermediate calculation of lateral and vertical velocities*
The use of fractionary steps on Eqs (9.3) and (9.4) makes it possible to introduce the auxiliary unknowns $\tilde{V}$ and $\tilde{W}$, defined by

$$\frac{\tilde{V} - V(x)}{\Delta x} + \frac{V}{U} \frac{\partial V}{\partial y} + \frac{W}{U} \frac{\partial V}{\partial z} = \frac{1}{U} \left[ \frac{\partial}{\partial y} \left( \nu_h \frac{\partial \tilde{V}}{\partial y} \right) + \frac{\partial}{\partial z} \left( \nu_z \frac{\partial \tilde{W}}{\partial z} \right) \right] \quad (9.16)$$

$$\frac{\tilde{W} - W(x)}{\Delta x} + \frac{V}{U} \frac{\partial W}{\partial y} + \frac{W}{U} \frac{\partial W}{\partial z} = \frac{1}{U} \left[ \frac{\partial}{\partial y} \left( \nu_h \frac{\partial \tilde{W}}{\partial y} \right) + \frac{\partial}{\partial z} \left( \nu_z \frac{\partial \tilde{W}}{\partial z} \right) - g \frac{\rho^*}{\rho_n} \right]$$

$$(9.17)$$

and

$$\frac{V(x + \Delta x) - \tilde{V}}{\Delta x} = - \frac{1}{\rho_n U(x)} \frac{\partial P^*}{\partial y} \quad (9.18)$$

$$\frac{W(x + \Delta x) - \tilde{W}}{\Delta x} = - \frac{1}{\rho_n U(x)} \frac{\partial P^*}{\partial z}. \quad (9.19)$$

Equations (9.16) and (9.17) are solved in the same way as Eq. (9.15) (except for gravity), in order to find $\tilde{V}$ and $\tilde{W}$. The conditions imposed on the latter are the boundary conditions selected for $V$ and $W$.

*Calculation of pressure*
By introducing Eqs (9.18) and (9.19) into the continuity equation, Eq.

(9.1), the following expression is obtained:

$$\frac{\Delta x}{\rho_n}\left[\frac{\partial}{\partial y}\left(\frac{1}{U}\frac{\partial P^*}{\partial y}\right)+\frac{\partial}{\partial z}\left(\frac{1}{U}\frac{\partial P^*}{\partial z}\right)\right]=\frac{U(x+\Delta x)-U(x)}{\Delta x}+\frac{\partial \bar{V}}{\partial y}+\frac{\partial \bar{W}}{\partial z}.$$

(9.20)

To solve this equation, boundary conditions must be imposed on $P^*$. These conditions must be derived from the chosen velocity conditions, using Eqs (9.3) and (9.4). However, the boundaries have a relatively small impact on our problem, which will enable us to simplify these conditions.

At the top and on the sides of the rectangular computing domain, the boundaries are assumed to be a relatively large distance from the jet. Therefore, a non-disturbance condition is imposed: $P^* = 0$. At ground level, in order to comply with the impermeability condition, the following expression is deduced from Eq. (9.13): $\partial P/\partial z = 0$. Equation (9.20) is then solved by double vectorial sweeping or by operator splitting with coordination, depending on the grid size, in order to find $P^*(x+\Delta x)$. $V(x+\Delta x)$ and $W(x+\Delta x)$ are then calculated, using Eqs (9.18) and (9.19).

## 9.3  Use of the model

### 9.3.1  Comparison with laboratory experiments

The eddy diffusivity laws used in this model have been adjusted (Viollet 1977) using the results of laboratory experiments (hydraulic flumes). Figure 9.5 gives an example of a comparison between results obtained from experiments and calculations for the same buoyant discharge (densimetric Froude number, $\mathbb{F}_0 = 0.8$), and different wind velocities. As shown on Fig. 9.6, the calculations served to point out the existence of eddies perpendicular to the axis of the plume, as well as the consequent U-shape deformation of the latter; this deformation may even result in the plume splitting into two parts.

Figures 9.7 and 9.8 display the results of calculations related to strongly stratified atmospheres, with and without wind respectively. The plume-stopping process caused by temperature inversion and the subsequent spreading of the plume into a thin layer are clearly reproduced in the calculations.

### 9.3.2  Comparison with natural observations of plumes from natural-draught cooling-towers

The comparison between calculations and observations was performed on a variety of discharge quantities, corresponding to power stations with capacities ranging from 250 MW (Gardanne, France, one cooling-tower) to 3000 MW (John Amos, USA, three cooling-towers). The results of this

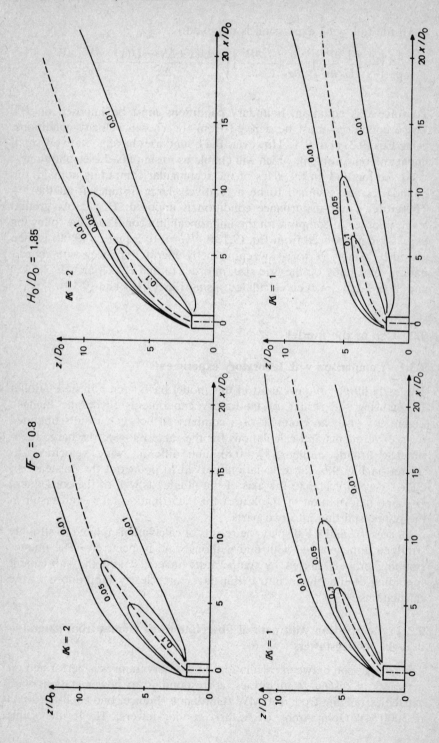

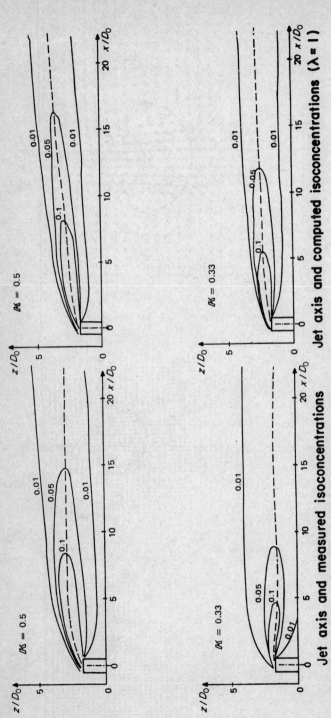

*Fig. 9.5*  Comparison of measured and calculated isoconcentrations

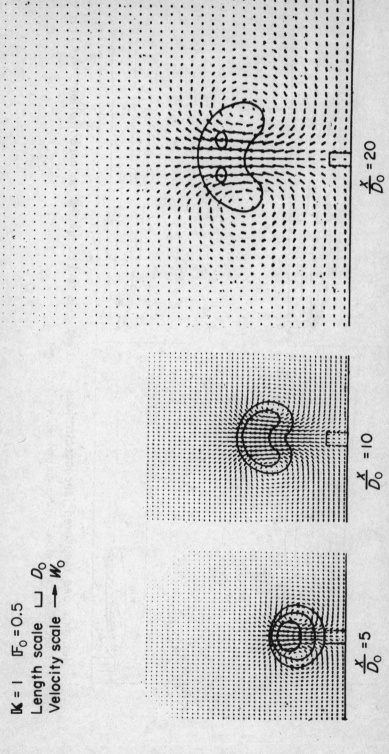

$\mathbb{K} = 1$  $\mathbb{F}_0 = 0.5$
Length scale ⊔ $D_0$
Velocity scale ⟶ $W_0$

$\dfrac{x}{D_0} = 5$  $\dfrac{x}{D_0} = 10$  $\dfrac{x}{D_0} = 20$

*Fig. 9.6* Velocity fields $(V, W)$ and isoconcentration curves 0.05 and 0.01 calculated in planes perpendicular to the cross-current

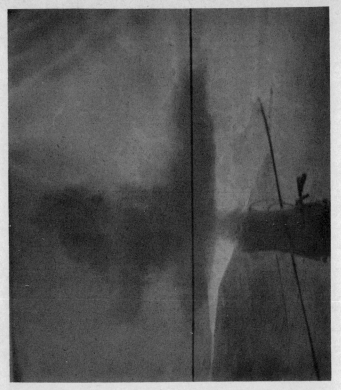

(b)

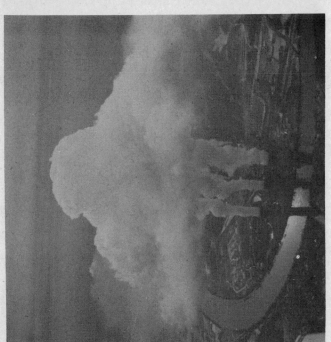

(a)

*Fig. 9.7* Evolution of buoyant jets in a stratified atmosphere in the absence of wind. (*a*) John Amos site; (*b*) flume test

149

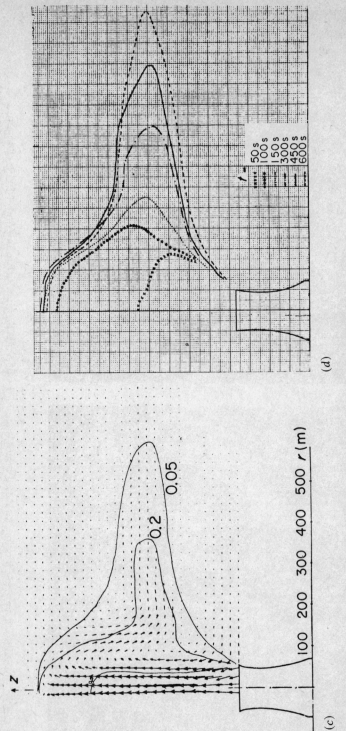

*Fig 9.7 (contd.)* (*c*) velocity field and main isoconcentrations at *t* = 450 s (calculated);
(*d*) evolution of the isoconcentration 0.05 (calculated)

(*c*)

0.05

0.2

100  200  300  400  500  *r* (m)

*z*

(*d*)

*t*

50 s
100 s
150 s
300 s
450 s
600 s

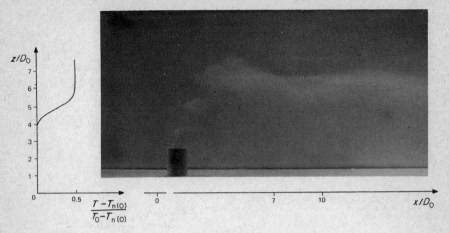

Photograph of the experiment

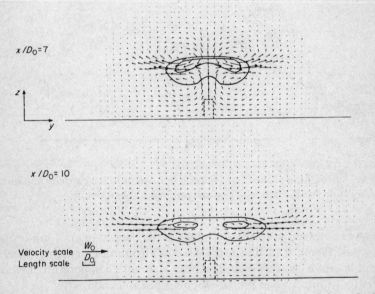

*Fig. 9.8* Velocities $(V, W)$ and isoconcentrations 0.05 and 0.01 calculated perpendicular to the cross-current: $\mathbb{F}_0 = 0.5$; $\mathbb{K} = 1$; $\mathbb{R}_0 = 3000$

comparison are summarized in Fig. 9.9 (Caudron and Viollet 1979). It should be underlined that, in the calculations relating to naturally occurring cases, the model adjustments previously made in the light of laboratory tests did not need to be modified.

Figures 9.10 and 9.11 provide a few comparison examples. Figure 9.10 highlights the predominant impact of the ambient relative humidity, when

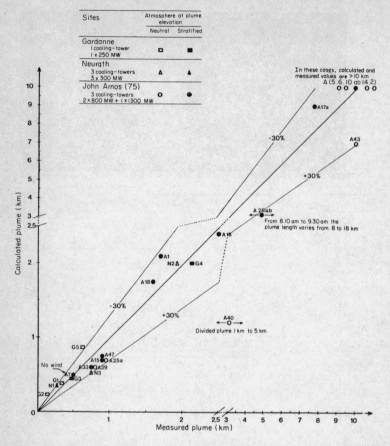

*Fig. 9.9* Verification of the 'Panach' code in relation to the capacity and number of cooling towers, and the ambient meteorological conditions

the power released is relatively small, under nearly neutral atmospheric conditions. Figure 9.11 illustrates the case of the three cooling-towers of the John Amos power station, where a severe temperature inversion results in a quite typical plume-stopping phenomenon.

## 9.4   Use of numerical models in impact studies

Practical application, within the scope of impact studies, can be found at various stages. First, as shown on Fig. 9.12, the model enables a comparison to be made under different typical meteorological conditions, and considering various cooling-tower layouts and types. Secondly, it can be used to make predictions on the type of plume to be obtained under

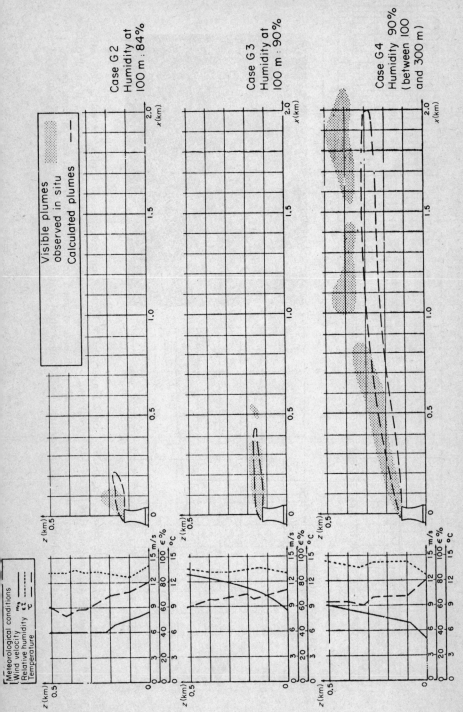

*Fig. 9.10*  Gardanne cooling-tower: influences of humidity

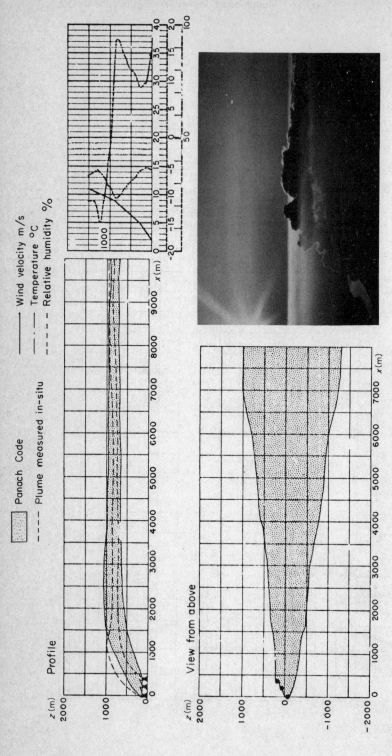

Key:

▨ Panach Code
---- Plume measured in-situ

—— Wind velocity m/s
—·— Temperature °C
---- Relative humidity %

*Fig. 9.11* Case 10A: John Amos station, at 08.11 on 2 January 1975. Three damp natural-draft cooling towers: $2 \times 800$ MWe + 1300 MWe; evacuated thermal capacity = 3700 MW (total load). The plume is stopped by a temperature inversion at an altitude of between 900 and 1300 m. Underneath this inversion, an almost adiabatic thermal gradient promotes the vertical entrainment of the ambient air, thus increasing the humidity under the stratification. A substantial stratus is thus obtained, whose length is up to 26 km in severe winter conditions

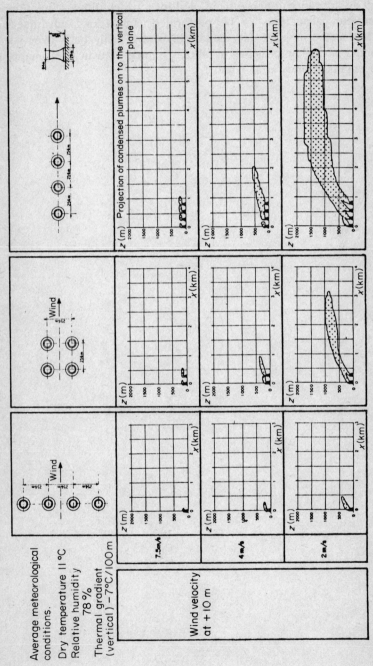

*Fig. 9.12.* Visible plumes from damp natural-draft cooling-towers. Influence of cooling-tower location versus wind direction and velocity

various typical, or highly unfavourable, meteorological conditions. Lastly, through an appropriate non-dimensional form which reduces the number of complete calculations to be performed, and taking advantage of processed meteorological data collected on a bi-daily basis over years, this model makes it possible to obtain annual statistical estimates of plume lengths (Darles *et al.* 1980).

# Conclusions

This book describes the present resources of the Laboratoire National d'Hydraulique for the study of certain environmental problems. Several widely different aspects are examined. In the field of marine and river engineering, we can mention, in particular, the calculation of tidal currents which, in some cases, are three-dimensional; the calculation of wave agitation in ports, the behaviour of which may be substantially non-linear; and, finally, river flow calculations which, more than any others, require an accurate definition of the boundaries and calculation field.

It is noted that the model and the method of numerical solution change according to the scale of the phenomenon to be studied, being fairly sophisticated in some cases. The results obtained in the field of tidal currents show the efficiency of numerical models which, even at a relatively small scale, are able to reproduce complex current patterns.

As regards the atmosphere, three scales are distinguished, leading to three models with different degrees of sophistication. The application of these models to the study of plumes from power-station cooling towers is described. In the immediate vicinity of the tower discharge, the flow is noticeably three-dimensional and no special assumption can be made. The selected model corresponds to the complete set of Navier–Stokes equations. At a greater distance, the plume—subjected to the action of the wind—can be represented by a model, for which, as the main assumption, the pressure gradient in the wind direction is neglected. This method results in a three-dimensional system which can be reduced to a set of two-dimensional problems. This model, which has been applied to numerous atmospheric plume configurations, has been proved to be effective, being suitable for reproducing the behaviour of the plume under very different atmospheric stability conditions.

Lastly, an analysis of the far field is outlined. A mesometeorological model has been designed and preliminary applications are already available. This tool should be used mainly to understand and interpret atmospheric field measurement surveys, which are always extremely limited.

Although they are applied to completely different problems, the models used in these two major fields obviously show common characteristics. The solution methods are very similar in the case of tidal currents and atmospheric plume calculations.

The suitability of numerical models for solving a wide range of problems is obvious but substantial improvements are still required if an accurate description of certain types of flow is sought. Paradoxically, it is easier to determine currents in the English Channel than in a port. At the Channel scale, a succinct description of the coast is sufficient and all the turbulent exchanges can be disregarded. In a port, the problem is not always two-dimensional, the description of the boundaries is very important and, in some cases, the turbulent exchanges play a leading role. The efforts that have been made should continue in this direction.

In the presence of complex geometrical characteristics, two methods can be used to obtain a satisfactory definition of the boundaries. The first method, which uses finite differences and a curvilinear grid, is illustrated by the case of river flows. The second method is based on finite elements. The latter, which has already been used for tide calculations, represents undoubtedly a new generation of numerical models with greater accuracy, but the cost of which is high, even if they are run on the fastest computers.

Modelling turbulent exchanges is still more complex. At present, the effect of density gradients, which have a pronounced impact on turbulence, is not very well understood and the design of a universal turbulence model still requires a lot of investigation. However, with a better definition of the boundaries, it becomes necessary to introduce a more sophisticated model. In the industrial hydraulics field, interesting results have been obtained in complex cases by using the turbulent energy and the rate of dissipated energy ($k-\varepsilon$ model), and the introduction of such parameter systems seems reasonable when studying environmental problems.

# References

Benqué, J-P. & Pernecker, L. (1980). 'Une tentative de calcul tridimensionnel, des champs de vitesse de pression et de témperature autour d'un réfrigérant. *XVI<sup>e</sup> Congrès SHF.*

Caudron, L. & Viollet, P-L. (1979). 'Les panaches d'aéroréfrigérants au voisinage des centrales thermiques'. *Météorologie*, No. 18, 67.

Charney, J. (1973). *Dynamic Meteorology*, Reidel Publishing Co.

Darles, A., Gland, A., Sabaton, M. & Viollet, P-L. (1980). 'Etude statistique tridimensionnelle des panaches d'aéroréfrigérants, *XVI<sup>e</sup> Congrès SHF.*

Davesne, M. (1978). *Modèle X–Z de la propagation de la marée et de la salinité dans un estuaire—application à l'estuaire de la Gironde*, Electricité de France Report, DER 42/78–38.

Daubert, A. (1974). *Notice d'utilisation du programme HYP1PL*, Electricité de France report, DER 41/74–12.

Daubert, A. & Graffe, O. (1967). 'Quelques aspects des écoulements presque horizontaux', *La houille blanche*, No. 8.

Dewagenaere, P. (1979). *Modèle tridimensionnel d'écoulements quasi horizontaux. Application aux phénomènes de mesométéorologie et à la courantologie des chevaux de navigation.* Thesis, P. et M. Curie University, Paris.

Esposito, P. (1979). *Tentatives de calculs tridimensionnels stationnaires et transitoires dans la cuve chaude de Super Phénix*, Electricité de France Report, E41/79.07.

Hauguel, A. (1978). 'A combined FE.BIE for water waves'. *Proc. 16th Internat. Conf. Coastal Engng.*

Hauguel, A. (1979). *Calcul des houles de tempêtes en eau peu profonde*, Electricité de France Report, DER HE 042/79.41.

Hauguel, A. & Lepetit, J-P. (1979). 'Dilution des eaux de rejet des centrales électriques en bord de Manche en France', *XVIII<sup>3</sup> Congrès de l'AIRH.*

Keramsi, A. (1978). *Résolution des équations de Navier–Stokes par une méthode de différences finies dans un maillage curviligne non-orthogonal*, Electricité de France Report E41/78.10.

Launder, B.E. (1975). 'On the effects of a gravitational field on the turbulent transport of heat and momentum', *J. Fluid Mech.*, 67.3.

Lions, J-L. & Marchouck, G-I. (1975). *Sur les méthodes numériques en sciences physiques et économiques*, Dunod.

Loh-Nien Fan. (1967). *Turbulent Buoyant Jets into Stratified or Flowing Ambient Fluid*, California Institute of Technology Report, KHR15.

Lomer, J.F. (1978). *La dérive en mers à marées*, Thesis, University of Paris.

Mary, D. *Modèle bidimensionnel d'écoulement utilisant les mailles curvilignes— application aux rivières*, Electricité de France Report (in preparation).

Thomson, J.F., Thames, F.C. & Martin, C.W. (1975). 'Numerical solution of the Navier–Stokes equations for arbitrary two-dimensional airfoils', *Conference on Aerodynamic Analysis Requiring Advanced Computers*, NASA, Lancley Research Center, Hampton, Virginia.

Turner, J.S. (1973). *Buoyancy Effects in Fluids*, Cambridge University Press.

Viollet, P-L. (1977). *Etude de jets dans les courants traversiers et dans les milieux stratifies*, Thesis, P.et M. Curie University, Paris.

Viollet, P-L., Keramsi, A. & Benqué, J-P. (1981). 'Modélisation bidimensionnelle d'écoulements en charge d'un fluide incompressible non-isotherme, *J. Mécanique*, **20**.

Warluzel, A. (1978). *Un modèle mathématique de transport et d'étalement d'une nappe d'hydrocarbure*, Electricité de France Report, DER HE 041/78.16.

Warluzel, A. & Benqué, J-P. (1979). 'Dispersion in a tidal sea', *11th Liége Colloquium on Ocean Hydrodynamics*.